Introduction to Chemistry

Department of Chemistry and Biochemistry

Florida Atlantic University, **Boca Raton FL**

Charles E. Carraher, Jr.

CENGAGE
Learning·

Australia • Brazil • Japan • Korea • Mexico • Singapore • Spain • United Kingdom • United States

Introduction to Chemistry:
Charles E. Carraher, Jr.

Senior Project Development Manager:
Linda deStefano

Marketing Specialist:
Courtney Sheldon

Senior Production/Manufacturing Manager:
Donna M. Brown

Production Editorial Manager:
Kim Fry

Sr. Rights Acquisition Account Manager:
Todd Osborne

For product information and technology assistance, contact us at
Cengage Learning Customer & Sales Support, 1-800-354-9706

For permission to use material from this text or product,
submit all requests online at **cengage.com/permissions**
Further permissions questions can be emailed to
permissionrequest@cengage.com

Compilation © 2012 Cengage Learning

ISBN-13: 978-1-285-38624-9

ISBN-10: 1-285-38624-8

Cengage Learning
5191 Natorp Boulevard
Mason, Ohio 45040
USA

Cengage Learning is a leading provider of customized learning solutions with office locations around the globe, including Singapore, the United Kingdom, Australia, Mexico, Brazil, and Japan. Locate your local office at:
international.cengage.com/region.
Cengage Learning products are represented in Canada by Nelson Education, Ltd.
For your lifelong learning solutions, visit **custom.cengage.com.**
Visit our corporate website at **cengage.com.**

Printed in the United States of America

Contents

Contents

Introductory to Chemistry

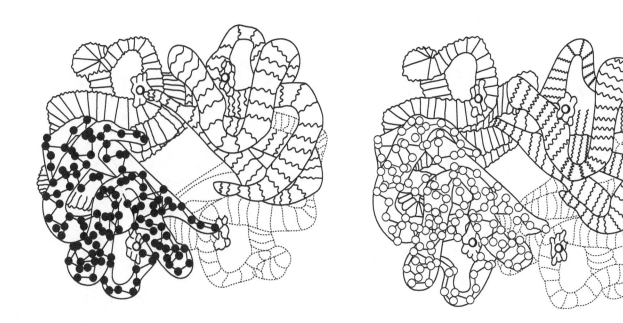

Charles E. Carraher, Jr.

Department of Chemistry and Biochemistry

Florida Atlantic University,
Boca Raton, FL

Introduction

There are many objectives to this book. They all revolve about preparing you to pass general chemistry. Among the objectives are tools that will give you a better chance to pass this course and other science courses. As we go along in our course we will touch on these tools. Some of the tools are to give you the mathematical skills necessary to solve simple algebraic and word problems. We call them simple but often they are not simple. Often the problem is more than possessing the mathematical skills, it is to know when to employ these skills. This takes logic and mapping out a strategy to solve the problem. We will work on both.

STUDYING CHEMISTRY

Studying chemistry is similar to studying any science. Following are some ideas that may assist you as you study.

Much of science is abstract. While much of the study of chemistry is abstract, it is easier to conceptualize, make mind pictures. One topic will be used to illustrate this. Polymers are large molecules that you come in contact with each day. They compose your skin, hair, plastic bags, paper, protein, nucleic acids, elastomers, fibers, rugs, curtains, etc. Because they are so familiar to you we will use polymers to illustrate studying chemistry. Think of what a polymer is and how it should behave. For linear polymers, think of a string or rope. Long ropes get entangled with themselves and other ropes. In the same way, polymer chains entangle with themselves and with chains of other polymers that are brought into contact with them. **Thus, create mental pictures of the polymer molecules as you study them or in your case smaller molecules such as water molecules.**

Chemicals and chemistry is real and all about us. We can look at molecules on a micro or atomic level or on a macroscopic level. The PET bottles we have may be composed of long chains of poly(ethylene terephthate), PET, chains. The aramid tire cord is composed of aromatic polyamide chains. Our hair is made up of complex bundles of fibrous proteins, again polyamides. **The chemistry you study is related to the real world in which we live. We experience "chemistry" at the macroscopic level everyday of our lives and this is a direct consequence of the atomic-level structure and behavior.** Make pictures in your mind that allow you to relate the atomic and macroscopic worlds.

At the introductory level we often examine only the primary factors that may cause particular behavior. Other factors may become important under particular conditions. **The molecules you study at times examine only the primary factors that impact polymer behavior and structure. Even so, these primary factors form the basis for both complex and simple structure-property behavior.**

The structure-property relationships you will be studying are based on well known basic chemistry and physical relationships. **Such relationships build upon one another and as such you need to study in an ongoing manner. Understand as you go along. Read the material BEFORE you go to class.**

This course is an introductory-level course. Each chapter or topic emphasizes knowledge about one or more areas. **Science has its own language. It is a language that requires you to understand and memorize certain key concepts.** Our memory can be short term or long term. Short term memory may be considered as that used by an actor or actress for a TV drama. It really does not need to be totally understood, nor retained after the final "take". **Long term memory is required in studying chemistry since it will be used repeatedly and is used to understand other concepts (that is, it is built upon).**

In memorizing, learn how you do this best-time of day, setting, etc. Use as many senses as necessary- **be active**-read your assignment, write out what is needed to be known, say it, listen to yourself say it. Also, look for patterns, create mnemonic devices, avoid cramming too much into too small a time, practice associations in all directions, and test yourself. **Memorization is hard work.**

While knowledge involves recalling memorized material, to really "know" something involves more than simple recall-it involves **comprehension**, **application**, **evaluation**, and **integration** of the **knowledge**. Comprehension is the interpretation of this knowledge, making predictions based on the knowledge, and applying the knowledge to different situations. Analysis involves evaluation of the information and comparing it with other information and synthesis has to do with integration of the information with other information.

In studying chemistry please consider doing the following—

- **skim the text BEFORE the lecture**
- **attend the lecture and take notes**
- **organize your notes and relate information**
- **read and study the assigned material**
- **study your notes and the assigned material and then**
- **review and self-test.**

Learning takes time and effort. Study daily skimming the text and other study material, think about it, visualize key points and concepts, write down important material, make outlines, take notes, study sample problems, etc. All of these help-but some may help you more than others-so focus on these modes of learning-but not at the exclusion of the other aspects.

In preparing for an exam consider the following—

- **accomplish the above-DO NOT wait until the day before the exam to begin studying; create good study habits**
- **study wisely- study how YOU study best-time of day, surroundings, etc.**
- **take care of yourself; get plenty of sleep the night before the exam**

- attend to last-minute details-is your calculator working, is it the right kind, do I have the needed pencils, review the material once again, etc.
- know what kind of test it will be-if possible and
- get copies of old exams if possible; talk to others that might have already had the course.

During the test

- stay cool, do NOT PANIC;
- read the directions; try to understand what is being asked for
- in an essay or similar exam work for partial credit; plan your answers
- in a multiple choice or T/F exam, eliminate obviously wrong choices
- look over the entire exam; work questions that you are sure of; then go to less sure questions; check answers if time permits.

The study of chemistry contains several types of content-

- **facts**-the term *polymer* means "many" (poly) "units" (mers).
- **concepts**-linear polymers are long molecules like a string
- **rules/equations/relationships-** density is mass per unit volume
- **problems**-what is the density of a material if 10 grams of it occupies 5 milliliters?

These varied types of content are often integrated within any topic, but in this introduction to chemistry, the emphasis is often on concepts and problems but all the aspects are important.

The major purpose of this course is to provide you with the tools necessary to pass General Chemistry.

Emphasis is on

- **Mastery of simple mathematics**
- **Skills to read problems**
- **Develop language**

Know what your are being graded on. Grading is often based on

- **Examinations**
- **Homework**
- **Attendance**

but it may also be based on participation in class and other activities.

Try to get to "know" your teacher. How do they teach and what signals may they give with respect to what they believe is important. Do they "telegraph" what will be on exams? The best way to see if they have "telegraphed" accurately what you should be studying is after the exam but that is too late. Another way is to visit with students that have already had the class and teacher to see their impressions.

Ask the teacher what is on the exam. See if they will give sample questions. Will they provide categories of questions that are included in the exam.

Remember that even the simple questions often require several steps. Chemistry is difficult but you will be provided the tools necessary to succeed in this book.

Our Chemical World

Science is the study of what is about us which we can measure in some manner. **Chemistry** is a study of matter and the changes it undergoes often on a molecular level. **Chemistry** is a central science important in most of the major issues today and integral in our everyday lives. Begin being more than passive in looking at your life and the issues of today to seeing how chemistry is important in understanding and making informed decisions.

Chemistry is often divided as to being basic or applied. This division is often artificial. Even so, **basic** research, often referred to as fundamental research, looks at fundamental, basic knowledge that underlay all of science. Basic research can lead to useful applications. **Applied** research is the application of basic/fundamental research results that affect our everyday lives in the pills we take, automobiles we drive, water we drink, food we eat, cloths we wear, etc.

You can begin to see that essentially all that we are and come into contact with in our live are chemicals and involve chemistry. Look at the ingredients in the things you buy and see what these ingredients contribute to the product. Begin looking at labels on you foods and medicines. You can get most of the information you need to do this from the web.

Chemicals all about us. They serve as the very basis of both plant and animal life as proteins, nucleic acids, and polysaccharides. In construction they serve as the concrete, insulation, and wooden and composite beams. At home they are found as the materials for our rugs, curtains, coatings, waste paper baskets, water pipes, window glass, ice cube trays, and pillows. In transportation they are present in ever increasing amounts in our air craft, automobiles, ships, and trucks. In communication they form critical components in our telephones, TVs, computers, CDs, newspaper, optical fibers, and cell phones. Chemicals in the form of plastics act as favorite materials for our toys such as toy soldiers, plastic models, toy cars, dolls, skip ropes, hula hoops and corvettes. Our food is polymer intense as meats, vegetables, breads, and cookies. In history polymers have been the vehicle for the Magna Carter, Torah, Bible, Koran, and our Declaration of Independence. Outside our homes they are present in our flowers, trees, soil, spider webs, and beaches. In fact, it is improbable that a chemical material is not involved in your present activity-reading a paper book, holding a plastic-intense writing device, sitting on a cloth-covered chair or bed, and if your eyes need corrective vision, glasses of one variety or another. The air we breathe is composed of chemicals such as nitrogen, oxygen, carbon dioxide, helium, hydrogen, etc.

To get an idea of the pervasiveness of materials in our everyday life, we can look at containers. Most containers are composed of large molecules called polymers. This includes glass, paper, and synthetic polymers. It is relatively easy to identify each of these general categories. Even within the synthetic polymer grouping, it has become relatively easy to identify the particular polymer used in some applications such as with disposable containers. Most of these synthetic polymers are identified by an "identification code" that is imprinted somewhere on the plastic container, generally on their bottom. The numbers and letters are described below. While the recycling code was developed by the Society of Plastics Industry for use with containers, today, the "chasing-arrows" triangle is being used more widely for recycling by the public. A colorless somewhat hazy water container has a '2' within the "chasing" arrows and underneath it "HDPE" both indicating the bottle is made of high density polyethylene. The clear, less flexible soda bottle has a '1' and "PETE" both signifying that the container is made out of poly(ethylene terephthalate), a polyester. A brownish clear medicine container has a '5' and the letters "PP" on its bottom conveying the information that the bottle is made of polypropylene. Thus, ready identification of some common items is easy.

PETE

Poly(ethylene terephthate)- **PET** or **PETE**
PET is the plastic used to package the majority of soft drinks. It is also used for some liquor bottles, peanut butter jars, and edible-oil bottles. About one-quarter of plastic bottles are PET. PET bottles can be clear; they are tough and hold carbon dioxide well.

HDPE

High-density polyethylene- **HDPE**
HDPE is a largely linear form of polyethylene. It accounts for over 50% of the plastic bottle market and is used to contain milk, juices, margarine, and some grocery snacks. It is easily formed through application of heat and pressure and is relatively rigid and low cost.

V

Poly(vinyl chloride)- **PVC** or **V**
PVC is used "pure" or as a blend to make a wide variety of products including PVC pipes, food packaging film, and containers for window cleaners, edible oils, and solid detergents. It accounts for only 5% of the container market.

LDPE

Low-density polyethylene- **LDPE**
LDPE has branching and is less crystalline, more flexible, and not as strong as HDPE. The greater amount of amorphous character makes it more porous than HDPE, but it offers a good inert barrier to moisture. It is a major material for films from which trash bags and bread bags are made.

PP

Polypropylene- **PP**
PP has good chemical and fatigue resistance. Films and fibers are made from it. Few containers are made of PP. It is used to make some screw-on caps, lids, yogurt tubs, margarine cups, straws, and syrup bottles.

PS

Polystyrene- **PS**
PS is used to make a wide variety of containers, including those known as "Styrofoam" plates, dishes, cups, etc. Cups, yogurt containers, egg cartons, meat trays, and plates are made from PS.

OTHER

Other Plastics
A wide variety of other plastics are coming to the marketplace including copolymers, blends, and multilayered combinations.

Figure 1.1 *Recycling code for common plastics.*

The Society of Plastics Industry recycling codes utilizing the numbers 1–7 and bold, capital letters to designate the material utilized to construct the container.

But, because of the use of many more complex combinations of polymers for many other items, such identification and identification schemes are not as straight forward. For some items, such as clothing and rugs, labels are present that tell us the major materials in the product. Thus, a T-shirt might have "cotton" on its label signifying that the T-shirt is largely made of cotton. A dress shirt's label may say 55% cotton and 45% polyester meaning it is made from two polymers. Some items are identified by tradenames. Thus, a dress advertised as being made from Fortrel (where "Fortrel" is a tradename) means it is made largely of a polyester material, probably the same polyester, PET or PETE, that made our soda bottle. Some everyday items are a complex of many materials only some or none noted. This is true for many running shoes and tires. Tires will often be described as being polyester (again, probably the same PETE) or nylon (or aramid). This describes only the composition of the tire cord but does not tell us what other materials are included in the tire's composition. Yet, those that deal with tires generally know what is used in the manufacture of the tire in addition to the "stated ingredients."

SCIENTIFIC METHOD

The **Scientific Method** involves observations, questioning, hypotheses, predictions and tests. All of these involve gathering information and interpreting it with some logic and knowledge. We really employ the scientific method when we cook. We see which ingredients and how much give us the particular food we want. Thus, in cooking chocolate chip cookies we might experiment with the ingredients, mixing, and cooking conditions and time. How much butter should we use and what kind. Which chocolate chips and how many should be use. We observe that a particular butter is good giving us desired fluffy cookies without burning the bottoms of the cookies leaving burnt cookie on the bottom of the pan. We than experiment, test, it to see if our observation holds. We use different cookie pans to see if our observation is more general and applies to lots of cookie pans. During this time we are making observations, questioning, making predictions (that the butter will give us soft cookies without burning the bottom of the pan), and gather information, all important in the scientific method.

Scientific Method- while it is often discussed in some formal context, we will note that it is something that you actually use in your everyday life. You make observations, test the observations, draw conclusions, readjust or refine your conclusions as you gather more information, etc.

Thus, I have left school to return to home at many different times. I found that if I leave between 4 to 4:30 that my trip home is faster. After further testing I found that the optimum time was actually 4:15 to 4:30. Thus, I try to leave during this time period.

CLASSIFICATION OF MATTER

Matter can be classified as follows. We need to be able to read such charts and relationships to see how the individual entries are related.

```
                              MATTER
                            ↙        ↘
                   PURE                    MIXTURE
                 ↙      ↘                 ↙        ↘
          Elements      Compounds   Homogeneous      Heterogeneous
```

What is an **element**? An element is matter that has only one kind of atom. It can be monoatomic or diatomic or more.

What is a **compound**? A compound has more than one kind of atom in it.

What is a **mixture**? Has more than one kind of matter in it.

What is a **homogeneous mixture**? Mixture of compounds and/or elements that are in the same phase. Homogeneous mixtures appear to be homogeneous or the same throughout.

What is a **heterogeneous mixture**? Mixture of compounds and/or elements that are separated from one another. Heterogeneous mixtures appear to be heterogeneous or unlike throughout.

While they are different, we will use mass (caused by weight of atoms) and weight (gravitational force) interchangeably.

MATTER-what occupies space and can be perceived by us.

MASS-quantity of matter in a material.

WEIGHT-force of gravity.

PHASES

Matter can also be divided according to being solid, liquid or gas. Solids, liquids and gases are called states of matter or **phases**. The volume of a material is the amount of space taken up by the material. The three major states of matter or phases are

Solids have a fixed or definite volume and shape. They are rigid and generally have the highest density of the three main phases.

Liquids have a definite volume and occupy the shape of the container but do not always fill the container. Liquids are relatively incompressible.

Gases occupy the entire volume of the container with no fixed shape and they are easily compressed.

PROPERTIES

PHYSICAL CHANGE- Change in form of matter but not chemical identity-melting, boiling.

PHYSICAL PROPERTY- Characteristic observed for a material without changing its chemical identity.

EXTENSIVE PROPERTY-magnitude depends on amount of material-mass and volume.

INTENSIVE PROPERTY-independent of amount of material-density, melting point, color.

CHEMICAL CHANGE- Change where the atoms are arranged in a different way; rearrangement of atoms from reactants to products.

CHEMICAL PROPERTY-Tendency to rearrange atoms in a chemical reaction.

PROBLEMS

1. Define chemistry.

2. Can the baking of sugar cookies be an example of the scientific method?

3. Name something that you come in contact with each day that is not composed of atoms.

4. Give an example of a heterogeneous mixture.

5. Give an example of a homogeneous mixture.

6. Give an example of a metal that is a liquid at room temperature.

7. The phase change of liquid water changing into solid water is called a(an)_____ change.

8. Is common table salt sodium chloride a compound? Why?

9. Is common sugar that is listed as 98% sugar a pure compound?

10. The conversion of hydrogen gas and oxygen gas into liquid water is a _____ change.

11. The color of gold is a _____ property.

12. The fact that gold seldom reacts with materials normally found in nature is a _____ property.

13. We are not able to see with our eye the atoms in air, does this mean that air does not contain matter?

14. Are all chemicals dangerous?

15. Give three examples of things you come in contact with that are composed of atoms.

16. What phase is ice in?

17. Which phase of water has a fixed volume and shape.

18. What are the three major phases of water?

19. Name three chemical compounds you come into contact with daily.

20. Since you cannot see the fizz in soda pop is it really a chemical.

ANSWERS

1. Define chemistry.

   Chemistry involves changes to the materials about us usually involving changes in the arrangement of atoms.

2. Can the baking of sugar cookies be an example of the scientific method?

   Yes, if we change the amount of sugar, cooking time, change the amount of butter, etc. and observe the differences in the texture and taste of the resulting cookie and continue to make changes looking for the "perfect" cookie.

3. Name something that you come in contact with each day that is not composed of atoms.

   Essentially all that we come in contact is made of atoms-water, air, food, computer, . . . but love and hate, desire, etc. are emotions and not composed of atoms but the emotions are actually the result of rearrangements of atoms within our brain, etc.

4. Give an example of a heterogeneous mixture.

   Salad dressing.

5. Give an example of a homogeneous mixture.

   Air.

6. Give an example of a metal that is a liquid at room temperature.

   Mercury.

7. The phase change of liquid water changing into solid water is called _____ change.

   Physical change or freezing.

8. Is common table salt sodium chloride a compound? Why?

   It is a compound because it contains more than one kind of atom, here sodium atoms and chloride (chlorine) atoms.

9. Is common sugar that is listed as 98% sugar a pure compound?

   No because it contains 2% of something other than common sugar.

10. The conversion of hydrogen gas and oxygen gas into liquid water is a _____ change.

    Chemical

11. The color of gold is a _____ property.

    Physical

12. The fact that gold seldom reacts with materials normally found in nature is a _____ property.

    Chemical

13. We are not able to see with our eye the atoms in air, does this mean that air does not contain matter?

    No, the atoms/molecules in air are simply too small for us to see.

14. Are all chemicals dangerous?

    No. In fact, most chemicals are used to aid society as buildings, roads, materials composing our computers, medicines, etc.

15. Give three examples of things you come in contact with that are composed of atoms.

    Essentially everything including our hands, feet, face, hair, food are composed of atoms.

16. What phase is ice in?

    Solid

17. Which phase of water has a fixed volume and shape.

    Solid

18. What are the three major phases of water?

Solid, liquid, gas

19. Name three chemical compounds you come into contact with daily.

Essentially everything we come in contact with are compounds. Some are more complex than others. Examples are air, gasoline, water, sugar, wood, plastic, polyethylene, polystyrene, hair, skin.

20. Since you cannot see the fizz in soda pop is it really a chemical.

Yes. It is carbon dioxide and is so small that you cannot see the individual molecules with your eye.

Measurement and Problem Solving

UNCERTAINITY

There is a limit to the certainty we have in making a measurement. By agreement, we typically note a measurement and add one additional figure that is an uncertain figure. Thus, let us say we are measuring the volume of a liquid using a graduated cylinder. We are careful to read that the liquid occupies 45 mL. We are not sure if the next value is a 0.8 but it appears so. Thus, we report the volume as 45.8 mL. We are pretty sure that the volume is 45 mL and not 46 or 44 mL but not so sure on the tenths of an mL.

SCIENTIFIC NOTATION

Because we can deal with very large and very small values in science we have developed a way to express these very large and very small values simply. This approach can also be used for everyday values.

Scientific notation is the reporting of a value with one figure to the left of the decimal point and additional figures to the right of the decimal point and the use of some power of ten. We will need to become familiar with scientific notation and how to report numbers using scientific notation. We will also need to know how to multiply and divide powers of ten. An additional aspect of scientific notation is worth noting. The value is reported to indicate our certainty of the measurement. Thus, for the volume of liquid in the cylinder noted above would be written as 4.58×10^1.

As noted above, a number expressed or written in scientific notation is simply the number written so that it contains one number followed by a period followed by the other numbers and this is multiplied by an appropriate power of ten. It is really simple. Thus, let us say we have 132 marbles. This is expressed in scientific notation as 1.32×10^2. If we have a bacteria that is 0.023 inches long then in scientific notation it is written as 2.3×10^{-2}.

We see that we can create the power of ten for values greater than 1 by simply counting the number of units we need to move over so that there is only one number to the left of the period. The number of times we move over is equal to the power of ten. Thus, there are about 683,000 people in South Dakota. If we know this to the thousand of people then the scientific notation is written as

$$6\ 8\ 3\ ,\ 0\ 0\ 0 = 6.83 \times 10^5$$

since we moved the "tens" marker or arrow to the left five places.

For values less than 1 we do a similar thing except we move the tens marker or arrow to the right. Thus, if the length of a particular hair on our head is 0.0000023 meters this is expressed in scientific notation as

$$0.0\ 0\ 0\ 0\ 0\ 2\ 3 = 2.3 \times 10^{-6}$$

Often we will simply give the number as a simple number such as there were 43 people at our party. While this can be expressed in scientific notation as 4.3×10^1 is would generally be simply given as 43 people.

Watch for this in exam and homework problems. You can generally tell if the number is to be expressed in scientific notation either by them telling you that they want the answer expressed in scientific notation or by what the possible answers. Thus, if they ask us what is 12×11 and the answers are a. 1.2×10^3; b. 1.32×10^2; c. 1.1×10^{-2}; d. 1.12×10^4 we know that they want the answer in scientific notation.

Again, a number written in scientific notation simply means that the value is written with one number to the left of the "." and the number is written to the appropriate power of ten. Here are some additional examples.

3400 becomes 3.4×10^3 55 becomes 5.5×10^1

0.0031 becomes 3.1×10^{-3} 0.000067 becomes 6.7×10^{-5}

560000000 becomes 5.6×10^8 0.0054 becomes 5.4×10^{-3}

MULTIPLICATION AND DIVISION OF POWERS OF TEN

We remember that for powers of ten $1/10^a$ is 10^{-a}. As we divide we retain the power of ten but change the sign. Thus $1/10^5$ is simply 10^{-5} and $1/10^{-3}$ is 10^3.

General $1/10^b = 10^{-b}$ ...

$1/10^4 = 10^{-4}$ ... or $1/10,000 = 1/10^4 = 10^{-4} = 0.0001$

General $1/10^{-b} = 10^b$ ...

$1/10^{-3} = 10^3$ ... or $1/0.001 = 1/10^{-3} = 10^3 = 1,000$

We multiple and divide powers of ten by simply adding the powers of ten. To determine the correct power of ten for $10^6 \times 10^{-4} \times 10^{-12} \times 10^8$ we simply add the powers of ten $6 + (-4) + (-12) + 8 = 6 - 4 - 12 + 8 = -2$. So that the product written in powers of ten is 10^{-2}. We can do this also in division remembering that in general $1/10^b$ is 10^{-b}. Thus, $10^{15}/10^{12}$ for the powers of ten is $15 - 12 = 3$ so the answer is 10^3. Remember that $1/10^{12} = 10^{-12}$.

General- Multiplication of Powers of Ten $A \times 10^a \times B \times 10^b = A \times B \times 10^{a+b}$

$3 \times 10^6 \times 2 \times 10^4 = 6 \times 10^{10}$ ...

$6 \times 10^{-4} \times 1.2 \times 10^{12} = 7.2 \times 10^8$ ...

General- Division of Powers of Ten $\quad A \times 10^a / B \times 10^b = (A/B) \times 10^{a-b}$ ...

$8 \times 10^6 / 2 \times 10^2 = 4 \times 10^4$ ...

$6 \times 10^5 / 3 \times 10^{-3} = 2 \times 10^8$ ...

$5 \times 10^{-3} / 2 \times 10^{-8} = 2.5 \times 10^5$ ...

Complex example $(8 \times 10^6 \times 6 \times 10^{-15}) / 1.5 \times 10^{-7} = 32 \times 10^{-2} = 3.2 \times 10^{-1}$

SIGNIFICANT FIGURES-WRITING NUMBERS TO REFLECT PERCISION

We should write numbers to reflect our confidence in them. Thus, a number
        53.72
means that we are certain of the first three numbers, 53.7 but am estimating the "2". The non-holding place holding digits in a measurement are called significant figures. We have rules telling us what are significant figures when we see a number. These rules are as follows.

1. all nonzero digits are significant. For instance
   70.34 has four significant figures. 0.0027 has two significant figures.

2. interior zeros (zeros between two numbers) are significant. For instance 56.003 has five significant figures. 0.00340075 has six significant figures.

3. trailing zeros, zeros after a decimal point, are significant. For instance 370.500 has six significant figures. 0.000560 has three significant figures.

4. leading zeros, zeros to the left of the first nonzero number, are not significant and only serve to locate the decimal point. For instance 0.00003560 has 4 significant figures.

5. interestingly, zeros at the end of a number but before a decimal point are ambiguous and should be avoided by using scientific notation where every figure given is written to note significance. For instance 56700 can have three, four, or five significant figures. If it has three significant figures then it would be written as 5.67×10^4; but if it has four significant figures it would be written as 5.670×10^4; or if it has five significant figures it would be written as 5.6700×10^4.

For multiplication and division the least significant figure determines, limits, the number of significant figures written in the answer. Thus, 5.0034 $\times$ 26 $\times$ 0.003304 is written as 0.43 with two significant figures since the figure with the least number of significant units is 26 with two significant units or digits.

ROUNDING OFF

As noted before, we write numbers to indicate the confidence we have in the number. Often we need to round off to the correct number of significant figures. Thus if we are given 56.78 we have three significant figures with the "8" being unsure. Should this be rounded off to 56.8 or 56.7? Or put in another way, should the scientific notation be written as 5.68 or 5.67×10^1?

We have rounding rules that tell us what to do, to round down so that this number would be 56.7 or to round up so the number is 56.8.

We round down if the digit that is unsure is 4 or less

4.52 rounds down to 4.5 and 16.74 rounds down to 16.7

And round up if the digit is 5 or more.

67.89 rounds up to 67.9 and 15.5 rounds up to 16.

UNITS OF MEASURE

Essentially all of the nations of the world have adopted the metric system to describe measurements. The lone major nation not to adopt it is the US. The metric system is referred to as the Systeme International d'Unites or SI units for short. It was developed in France in the 18th century and adopted by most of the countries of the world in the 1960s. The metric system is known as a decimalized system where conversion is easily made using a series of prefixes in multiples of ten employed to derive larger and smaller units. Table 2.1 contains some of the most common prefixes. Today, we live in a metric world with talk of the nano world. As we see in Table 1 nano is one of the prefixes used to convert to smaller units. The size of atoms is about a nanometer in diameter. So as we today are dealing with atoms and molecules whose dimensions are in the nanometer range we call this the nano world, or attach the prefix nano to what ever we are referring to that has similar dimensions.

Table 2.1 *Common prefixes.*

Prefix	Symbol	Decimal Equivalent	Exponential Equivalent
Teta-	T	1,000,000,000,000.	10^{12}
Giga-	G	1,000,000,000.	10^9
Mega-	M	1,000,000.	10^6
Kilo-	**k**	**1,000.**	$\mathbf{10^3}$
Deci-	d	0.1	10^{-1}
Centi-	**c**	**0.01**	$\mathbf{10^{-2}}$
Milli-	**m**	**0.001**	$\mathbf{10^{-3}}$
Micro-	**μ**	**0.000001**	$\mathbf{10^{-6}}$
Nano-	**n**	**0.000000001**	$\mathbf{10^{-9}}$
Pico-	p	0.000000000001	10^{-12}

As noted above, the metric system has an advantage over the US system in that conversions from one scale to another is simply done by multiplying or dividing by some unit of 10 whereas the US system is not as easy. Thus, there are 12 inches in one foot, 3 feet in one yard, and 5,280 feet in one mile.

The metric system is particularly used for volume, distance, and weight measurement but the time units are similar in the SI and US systems. Table 2.2 contains some of the common units for distance, volume and weight along with the associated prefixes.

Table 2.2 *Common SI units in distance, volume, and weight.*

Distance	
Kilometer-km meter-m	centimeter-cm millimeter-mm
Volume (note that 1 mL = 1 cubic milliliters = 1 cc = 1cm³)	
Liter-l	milliliter-mL
Weight	
Kilogram-kg	gram-g milligram-mg nanogram-ng

Table 2.3 *Common equivalence values.*

Physical Quantity	Metric Unit	Abbreviation	US Unit Equivalent
Length	Kilometer	km	1 km = 0.62 mile
	Meter	m	1 m = 1.09 yard
	Centimeter	cm	1 cm = 0.39 inches
Mass	Kilogram	kg	1kg = 2.2 pounds
	Gram	g	1 g = 0.035 ounce
Volume	Liter	L	1L = 1.057 quart
	Milliliter	mL	1 mL = 0.0339 fluid ounce

DERVIATION OF CONVERSION UNITS

Let us first see how we can make conversion factors from know equivalences. We know that 12 inches = 1 foot. We can divide both sides by 12 inches giving

$$\frac{12 \text{ inches}}{12 \text{ inches}} = \frac{1 \text{ foot}}{12 \text{ inches}} = 1$$

This allows us to multiple any number of inches by the conversion factor (1foot/12 inches) and obtain the number of feet. We can do this because multiplying anything by one does not change the value. Thus, 48 inches is ___ feet. Let us multiple 48 inches by our conversion factor giving us

$$48 \text{ inches} \times \frac{1 \text{ foot}}{12 \text{ inches}} = 4 \text{ feet}$$

Since the dimension "inch" appears above and below they cancel giving us the answer in "feet."

We can also derive the conversion unit that allows us to convert from feet to inches by a similar manner. Again, 12 inches = 1 foot. Divide both sides by 1 foot gives

$$\frac{12 \text{ inches}}{1 \text{ foot}} = \frac{1 \text{ foot}}{1 \text{ foot}} = 1$$

Thus, 12 feet = ___ inches. Multiple 12 feet by our conversion factor giving us 12 feet × (12 inches/1 foot) = 144 inches.

We can do this for the equivalence that 1 yard = 0.914 meters. Dividing both sides by 1 yard gives us

$$\frac{1 \text{ yard}}{1 \text{ yard}} = \frac{0.914 \text{ meters}}{1 \text{ yard}} = 1$$

Again, we can calculate the number of meters in any given number of yards by multiplying the number of yards by 0.914 meters/1 yard. Thus, the number of meters in 32.0 yards is

$$32.0 \text{ yards} \times \frac{0.914 \text{ meters}}{1 \text{ yard}} = 32.9 \text{ meters}$$

And, we can also divide both sides of the equivalence 1 yard = 0.914 meters by 0.914 meters and get

$$\frac{1 \text{ yard}}{0.914 \text{ meters}} = \frac{0.914 \text{ meters}}{0.914 \text{ meters}} = 1$$

so that we can multiply the number of meters by 1 yard/0.914 meters to obtain the number of yards. Thus, there are ___ yards in 28 meters. Multiple 28 meters by the conversion factor gives 28 meters × (1 yard/0.914 meters) = 31 yards.

We can also do this with using metric equivalences. Thus, 1g = 1,000 mg. How many grams are in a 400 mg pill? We derive our conversion factor by dividing both sides by 1,000 (or 10^3) mg giving

$$\frac{1 \text{ g}}{1,000 \text{ mg}} = \frac{1,000 \text{ mg}}{1,000 \text{ mg}}$$

We then multiple 400 mg by our conversion factor giving

$$400 \text{ mg} \times \frac{1 \text{ gram}}{1,000 \text{ mg}} = 0.400 \text{ g}$$

SI CONVERSIONS

To illustrate the ease of conversion within the metric system look at the following.

1. The mass of a grain of sand is about 0.001 grams or 1 mg.

2. The weight of a person is 100,000 grams or 100 kg.

3. The volume of a golf ball is about 0.001 l or 1 mL.

4. A virus has a length of about 0.0000001 m or 100 nm and a weight of 0.000000000001 grams or 0.001 ng.

5. The distance from Vermillion South Dakota to Sioux City Iowa is 75 miles or 139 km.

6. The height of a man 6 fool tall is 1.83 meters.

7. A 30 pound sack of potatoes weights 13.6 kg.

   It is of note that because the density of water is 1 g/mL that by knowing the volume of water we can calculate its weight by simply converting our volume to milliliters and then multiply by 1. Density is m/V and through cross multiplication we have that m = D × V. Thus, the mass of 36 mL of water is m = 1 g/mL × 36 mL = 36 g or simply multiply the volume in milliliters by 1 and use the unit gram for the answer.

8. The weight of 45 mL of water is 45 g.

9. The weight of 2 liters of water is 2,000 g. Remember to convert 2 liters to milliliters. Also, remember since the density of water is 1 gram/milliliter or 1 g/mL the volume of water in milliliters is also the weight in grams.

Thus, 2 liters × 1000 mL/L = 2,000 mL   and
2,000 mL × 1 gram/mL = 2,000 grams

For complex conversions we can develop a "road map" or "solution map" that describes the individual steps we need to take to accomplish the calculations. Thus, if we know that there are 1,000 g in 1 kg and 100 cg in a g how many kg are there in 600 cg?

We are given cg and want to go to kg. We know this because the problem tells us this. How many kg are in 600 cg. We want to go from **cg → to kg**. We do not know the direct conversion factor from cg to kg so we will have an intermediate step that can be described as **cg → g → kg**. This **cg → g → kg** is described as a road map or solution map.

To do this we will set up the necessary conversions as follows:

$$600 \text{ cg} \times \frac{1 \text{ g}}{100 \text{cg}} \times \frac{1 \text{kg}}{1,000 \text{ g}} = 0.006 \text{ kg}$$

Notice how the units cancel as we go along the road map.

DENSITY

Archimedes, an ancient Greek philosopher, engineer, and mathematician, in about 250 BC was given the job by King Hiero to determine if a new crown in the shape of a laurel wreath was made out of gold or some other material. He had to do this without damaging the crown. Silver and other materials were added by dishonest goldsmiths. The density of silver (10.5 g/mL) is about one half that of gold (19.3 g/mL) so the density of a solid gold wreath would be greater than that of a gold-silver mixture. Archimedes was taking a bath at the public bath works and noticed that the level increased as he entered the pool. It dawned on him that he had found how to answer the king's request. It is said that he took off from the pool running in the streets naked yelling "Eureka" which is roughly translated as "I found it." What he found was not how to determine density but rather how to determine the volume of irregularly shaped objects such as the ornate crown. In the following problems you will be given two of the three values needed to determine density, volume, or weight.

Density is the mass/volume. You need to know how to work this relationship.

D = M/V Through cross multiplication you get M = DV and though division of both sides by D you get V = M/D. Look at the units.

Know density = mass/volume and how to determine any one of the three-mass, volume or density given the other two. D = M/V; M = DV; & V = M/D

What is the volume of 50 grams of a material with a density of 2 g/ml

A. V = M/D = 50 g/2g/ml = 25 ml

Q. What is the density of a material that weighs 30 grams and occupies a volume of 10 ml?

A. D = M/V = 30 g/10 ml = 3 g/ml

Q. What is the weight of 40 ml of a material with a density of 4 g/ml?

A. M = DV = 4 g/ml × 40 ml = 160 g

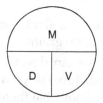

The circle above is an easy way to remember the relationships between mass, density, and volume. Place your finger over the desired quantity and the relationship between the other two is given. Thus, place your finger over "D" and you have M/V so density is mass divided by volume; place your finger over "M" and you have DV so that mass is density times volume.

DIMENSIONAL ANALYSIS- ONCE AGAIN

Dimensional analysis is an approach to help us know if we are performing the right or correct mathematical operations. Some numbers have what we call "units". Thus, the number 8 can be 8 centimeters, 8 kilograms, 8 chickens, 8 centimeters/seconds. The descriptors after the number "8" are the units-centimeters, kilograms, chickens, and centimeters/seconds. It can also have no dimension being simply the number "8". Science has lots of relationships that we express by formula. Thus, the density of a material is defined as the weight or mass per unit volume or D=m/v. The units on one side of the "=" sign must be the same as the units on the other side. The units for density are mass/volume. So for the expression

$$D = m/v \text{ we have the units}$$

$$\text{mass/volume} = \text{mass/volume}$$

so that they are the same units on both sides of the "=" sign.

We need to remember that the same thing-number or unit-that is in both the numerator and denominator cancel themselves out. Thus how many is 10 atoms divided by 10 atoms; we have 10 atoms/10 atoms = 1. Here, both the number and units have exactly canceled themselves out.

Question. If you were to be running a 2000 meter run about a 400 meter track (that is one lap about the track is 400 meters), how many laps would you have to run.

The general equation is

# of laps = distance run/distance each lap is = 2000 meters/400 meters/lap = 5 laps.

Here, the units "meters" are the same in the numerator and denominator so they cancel leaving the unit 1/1/laps which is simply "laps".

We need to master converting from one unit to another. In science we typically use what is referred to as "SI" units . You need to know the prefix relationships and the fundamental units. You also need to be able to do simple calculations moving from one unit to another and moving from one grouping of units to another grouping of units one step at a time. **This takes practice.**

You need to know how to "create" units or "conversion factors" from given relationships. Thus, if there are 2.54 centimeters in an inch we can write this as 2.54 cm in one in (using the abbreviation "cm" for centimeters and "in" for inch) or as

$$2.54 \, cm = 1 \, in$$

Now we can divide (or multiple) each side by the same thing and not change the relationship. Thus we can divide both sides by "1 in" giving us

$$2.54 \, cm/1 \, in = 1 \, in/1in = 1$$

and we can divide both sides by 2.54 cm giving

$$2.54 \, cm/2.54 \, cm = 1 \, in \, /2.54 \, cm = 1.$$

We now have two conversion factors or combination of units (2.54 cm/1 in and 1 in/2.54 cm) that we can use whenever we need to convert or change a value from "cm" to "in" or "in" to "cm".

Question. How many cm are there in 12 inches? We can set up a little map telling us where we are and where we want to go with respect to the units. The map might look like

$$in \rightarrow cm$$

We have two conversion factors showing us the relationship between "in" and "cm". We will use the wrong conversion factor first to show you what happens.

$$12 \, in \times (1 \, in/2.54 \, cm) = 4.7 \, in^2 \, /cm$$

In choosing the wrong conversion we did now end up with the correct unit "cm" but rather came up with a more complex set of units, we did what is commonly called "compounded" our units.

Now we will choose the correct unit to be used in this problem.

$12 \, in \times (2.54 \, cm/1 \, in) = 30 \, cm$. The "in / in" unit canceled themselves since one was in the numerator and the other "like" unit in the denominator.

Question. How many inches are in 100 cm? We do the same as above but choose the other conversion factor.

$$100 \, cm \, (1 \, in/2.54 \, cm) = 39 \, in.$$

We choose the conversion factor that allows us to cancel the "unwanted" unit. If the unit that we want to cancel is in the numerator then we choose a conversion factor where the unit is in the denominator. Conversely, if the "unwanted" unit is in the denominator we chose a conversion where that unit is in the nominator.

Question. How many minutes are there in 360 seconds. We know that there are 60 seconds in each minute or 60 seconds/minute or that there are 1/60 minute/seconds (simply the inverse of 60 seconds/minute).

Let us first draw a little map from where we are to where we want to go. Here it is we want to go from seconds → minutes. Since we want to cancel seconds we will want to use the relationship between seconds and minutes that will have "seconds" in the denominator so we can cancel it. Thus we will use the relationship 1/60 minute/seconds giving us

$$360 \, seconds \times 1/60 \, minute/seconds = 6 \, minutes.$$

Question. A fast runner can cover 400 meters in 55 seconds. How many meters per minute is this?

Thus we want to go from 400 meters/50 seconds to ? Meters/minute. Our road map might look like

$$\text{seconds} \rightarrow \text{minutes}.$$

Our starting value is created by simply dividing 400 meters by 55 seconds giving

$$400 \text{ meters}/55 \text{ seconds} = 7.3 \text{ meters/second}.$$

For our relationship we want to eliminate seconds replacing it with minutes and since seconds is in the denominator we want to use the relationship

$$60 \text{ seconds/minute}$$

since seconds is in the numerator and will cancel out.

Thus we have

7.3 meters/second $\times$ 60 seconds/minute = 438 meters/minute or 4.38 $\times$ 10^2 meters/minute.

Question. Next, if the runner can cover 400 meters in 55 seconds, how many centimeters per minute is this?

Again, we can establish a road map. It will be a two-step road map. We can start at converting the meters to centimeters or seconds to minutes.

$$\text{meters/second} \rightarrow \text{centimeters/second} \rightarrow \text{centimeters/minute}$$

We have the relationship between meters and centimeters as 100 centimeters = 1 meter or 100 centimeters/meter OR the inverse 1/100 meter/centimeters. In the first step we want to eliminate meters changing it to centimeters. Since the starting figure is 7.3 meters/second where meters is in the numerator, we want to use the relationship between meters and centimeters where meters is in the denominator so we can cancel it.

7.3 meters/second $\times$ 100 centimeters/meter = 730 centimeters/second.

Now we will do the second part converting 1/seconds to 1/minutes.

730 centimeters/second $\times$ 60 seconds/minute = 44,000 centimeters/minute or 4.4 $\times$ 10^4 centimeters/minute.

Together this would give us

7.3 meters/second $\times$ 100 centimeters/meter $\times$ 60 seconds/minute = 4.4 $\times$ 10^4 centimeters/minute.

You need to practice dimensional analysis.

We also need to create units sometimes. Thus, we need to be able to go from centimeters to centimeters squared to centimeters cubed or cubic centimeters, cc.

Question. A fish tank holds 3 cubic meters of water. How many cubic centimeters, cc, is this.

We know that 100 centimeters = 1 meter. Let us cube **both** sides we get

$100 \times 100 \times 100$ centimeters cubed = $1 \times 1 \times 1$ meter cubed or 10^6 cubic centimeters = 1 cubic meter = 1 meter cubed or 10^6 cubic centimeter/cubic meter or $1/10^6$ cubic meter/cubic centimeter or 10^{-6} cubic meter/cubic centimeter.

Thus we have 3 cubic meters $\times$ 10^6 cubic centimeters/cubic meter = 3 $\times$ 10^6 cubic centimeters.

PROPORTIONS AND CROSS-MULTIPLICATION

One way to solve a number of problems is to use proportions where all but one of the items is know. We solve for this unknown using cross-multiplication and solving for the unknown item.

Following is a simple portion in general terms.

$$\frac{a}{c} = \frac{b}{d}$$

Cross-multiplication gives a × d = c × b. We can now solve for any of the letters. For instance, if we are making batter for pancakes and the recipe calls for 1 cup of flour to make 6 pancakes, but we want to make 18 pancakes how many cups of flour should we use?

This is set up in the proportion approach as follows:

$$\frac{1 \text{ cup flour}}{X \text{ cups flour}} = \frac{6 \text{ pancakes}}{18 \text{ pancakes}}$$

Cross-multiplication gives 1 cup flour × 18 pancakes = X cups flour × 6 pancakes.

Solving for X we get X cups flour = 1 cup flour × 18 pancakes/6 pancakes = 3 cups flour

Let us solve another problem. The directions in an experiment calls for addition of 10 grams of sodium chloride, common table salt, to make 100 mL solution to make a salt water solution. We want to make 300 mL of solution of salt water with the same concentration of sodium chloride. How much sodium chloride should be added?

This can be set up in a proportion approach as follows:

$$\frac{10 \text{ grams salt}}{X \text{ grams salt}} = \frac{100 \text{ mL solution}}{300 \text{ mL solution}}$$

Cross-multiplication gives X grams salt × 100 mL solution = 10 grams salt × 300 mL solution and solving for X gives X grams salt = 10 grams salt × 300 mL solution / 100 mL solution = 30 grams salt.

PROBLEMS

1. What is $0.0000350 \times 1.65 \times 10^{12}$ divided by 1.45×10^{-12}? Give the answer to two significant figures in scientific notation.

2. A green rock with red strips was submerged in a graduated cylinder filled with heptane with a reading of 65.2 mL. The rock was removed giving a new reading of the heptane only of 60.0 mL. It has a density of 3.4 g/cc. What is the weight of the rock? It is toxic and needs to be kept from water.

3. How many significant figures are there in the following numbers?

   0.005600

   1.5340×10^{-23}

   453.

   672300

4. Write in scientific notation 0.002304 to three significant numbers.

5. It takes 4.0 kjoules (kj) of energy to lift 3 test tubes. How many joules is this?

   How many joules will it take to lift 5.0×10^4 test tubes?

6. As part of a drug experiment, a drug company synthesizes 3.00 kg of a drug. How many 250 mg pills can be made from this?

7. What is 4.25×10^{-6} times 1.6×10^{-4} divided by 2.56×10^{-5}? Write the answer in scientific notation. How many significant figures should the answer have?

8. How many centimeters are in 45 meters?

9. What is 6×10^{-6} divided by 3×10^{-2}?

10. How many 250 mg pills can be made from 200 grams?

11. A block that is blue colored and somewhat soft takes 2 kjoules to move up a hill; how many kjoules will it take to move 20 blocks of the same size up the same hill? The hill is 30 degrees and 200 meters long.

12. Give a solution map for converting kg to mg.

13. What is 4.00×10^6 times 2.00×10^{-3} divided by 1.0×10^4 written in scientific notation with two significant figures?

14. How many significant figures are in the following?

    0.003470

    7500

    3.450×10^3

15. What is the mass of a rock whose density is 4 g/ml if it occupies a volume of 200 cc?

16. A swimming pool was filled with water. It held 1×10^8 mL. How many kiloliters is this?

17. What are the basic SI units for weight, length, and volume?

18. Work is often measured in joules. How many kilojoules is needed to pick 20 bushels of weeds if it takes 3 millijoules to pick one bushel of weeds?

19. The radioactivity of a rock is 8,000 counts per seconds. How many counts is this per hour?

20. A car is traveling 60 kilometers per hour. How many centimeters per second is this?

21. A car is traveling at 100 kilometers/hour is traveling at _____ millimeters/second.

22. If the weight of one molecule of a material is 1.8×10^{-20} grams what is the weight of 6×10^{23} of this molecule?

23. For the above molecule, what is the weight of one molecule in kilograms?

24. How many milligrams are in 2 kilograms?

25. How many nanograms are in 50 grams?

26. How many significant figures are there in the number 3,402?

27. How many significant figures are there in the number 0.000003004?

28. What is the density of air where 22,400 mL weights 4 grams? Give the answer to one significant figure in scientific notation.

29. What is the answer to the problem 2.02×10^6 times 4.0×10^{-4} and this divided by 3.000×10^{16}? How many significant figures should the answer contain?

30. What is 3.02×10^{-3} squared? What kind of unit might this be if the value is given as 3.02×10^{-3} inches and you are asked to square it? Volume, length, area?

31. A rock displaces 13 mL of ethylene glycol and weights 4.03 grams. What is its density?

32. What is the weight of a rock whose volume is 35 cc and whose density is 7.2 g/mL?

ANSWERS

1. What is $0.0000350 \times 1.65 \times 10^{12}$ divided by 1.45×10^{-12}? Give the answer to two significant figures in scientific notation.

   One approach is to separate the non-ten to some power numbers from the power of ten numbers and work each part separately and then combine the results. First, let us write all of the numbers in scientific notation. The first number is the only one not already written in scientific notation. 0.0000350 is then 3.50×10^{-5}

   Second, let us group the non-powers of ten numbers— $3.5 \times 1.65/1.45 = 3.982758... = 4.0$ rounded off and to two significant figures.

   The powers of ten are then $10^{-5} \times 10^{12} / 10^{-12} = 10^{-5} \times 10^{12} \times 10^{12}$ To calculate the powers of ten we simply add the powers of ten $-5 + 12 + 12 = 19$ so the power of ten value is 10^{19}. Now we combine the two sets together to get the answer 4.0×10^{19}

   Remember $1/10^a$ is 10^{-a} so

   $1/10^6 = 10^{-6}$

   $1/10^{-15} = 10^{15}$

   and that multiplying exponents is achieved by simply adding the powers of ten.

   $10^6 \times 10^3 \times 10^{-5} = 10^{6+3+(-5)} = 10^{6+3-5} = 10^4$

2. A green rock with red strips was submerged in a graduated cylinder filled with heptane with a reading of 65.2 mL. The rock was removed giving a new reading of the heptane only of 60.0 mL. It has a density of 3.4 g/cc. What is the weight of the rock? It is toxic and needs to be kept from water.

   Remember to do density problems you need to know two of the three-weight (mass), volume, and density. Thus, ideas that a rock is toxic and needs to be kept from water might be nice to know but do not help us in solving the problem. Likewise, the observation that it is green with red strips is not helpful in solving the problem.

   Volume is not directly given but remembering that materials displace their volume in a liquid, often water for us but it could be another liquid such as carbon tetrachloride or kerosene or ethanol, we get the rock's volume from simply subtracting the liquids original volume from the volume when the rock is present giving 65.2 mL - 60.0 mL = 5.2 mL.

Rearranging the basic definition for density being D = M/V for M we get M = DV = 3.4 g/cc × 5.2 mL = 3.4 g/mL × 5.2 mL = 17.68 g or to two significant figures 18 g.

Remember that the units cc = cm^3 = mL.

3. How many significant figures are there in the following numbers?

0.005600   4 significant figures-numbers, including zeros, are significant in numbers less than 1.

$1.5340 × 10^{-23}$ 5 significant figures- since this is written in scientific notation then all numbers in front of the power of ten are significant

453.   3 significant figures. If there is a "." present then all numbers are significant, even if they are "0". Thus, 3600. has 4 significant figures.

672300   Do not know-since there is not a "." present we do not know if all or any of the zeros are significant.

4. Write in scientific notation 0.002304 to three significant numbers.

$2.30 × 10^{-3}$

Since the fourth number is less than 5 the zero remains a zero.

5. It takes 4.0 kjoules (kJ) of energy to lift 3 test tubes. How many joules is this?

Focusing on the prefix "kilo" which is 1000; thus 1000 J = 1 kJ or 10^{-3} kJ = 1 J

Next, we want to change kJ → J using the correct conversion value.

4.0kJ × 1000 J/1 kJ = 4,000 J = $4 × 10^3$ J.

In an exam, when answers are given they may be written in powers of ten as $4 × 10^3$ J or without the use of powers of ten as 4,000 J or 4000 J. All three of these answers are correct unless directed in the problem to give the answer in some form.

How many joules will it take to lift $5.0 × 10^4$ test tubes?

Probably the easiest way to work this type of problem is to use proportions. For this problem it would be

$$\frac{4.0kJ}{X\ kJ} = \frac{3\ test\ tubes}{4 × 10^4\ test\ tubes}$$

Solving for X we have 3 X = $4.0 × 5.0 × 10^4$ and X = $4.0 × 5.0 × 10^4/3$ = $6.7 × 10^4$ rounding off the answer to two significant figures.

6. As part of a drug experiment, a drug company synthesizes 3.00 kg of a drug. How many 250 mg pills can be made from this?

First thing is to change the units so that they will be the same. We can change kg to mg or mg to kg. Let us change the kg to mg. We can put down a little map that tells us what we need to do for the conversion. Here that road map might be

$$kg → g → mg.$$

We have memorized that there are 1000 g in a kg and 1000 mg in a gram. From this we will use the correct conversion factor to move us from kg to mg.

$3 \text{ kg} \times 1{,}000 \text{ g/kg} \times 1{,}000 \text{ mg/g}$ or $3 \text{ kg} \times 10^3 \text{ g/kg} \times 10^3 \text{ mg/g} = 3 \times 10^6 \text{ mg}$ or

$$3 \text{kg} \times \frac{1{,}000 \text{ g}}{1 \text{ kg}} \times \frac{1{,}000 \text{ mg}}{1 \text{ g}} = 3 \times 10^6 \text{ mg}$$

We can now use our proportion method to obtain the answer. We know that 1 pill takes 250 mg, so how many 250 mg pills can we make from 3×10^6 mg? In proportions this might be written as

$$\frac{1 \text{ pill}}{X \text{ pills}} = \frac{250 \text{ mg}}{3 \times 10^6 \text{ mg}}$$

Cross multiplication and solving for X we have

$X = 3 \times 10^6 / 250 = 3 \times 10^6 / 2.5 \times 10^2 = 1.2 \times 10^4 = 12{,}000$ pills

7. What is 4.25×10^{-6} times 1.6×10^{-4} divided by 2.56×10^{-5}? Write the answer in scientific notation. How many significant figures should the answer have?

   Again, let us separate out the non-powers of ten terms from the powers of ten terms. For the non-powers of ten terms we have

   $$4.25 \times 1.6 / 2.56 = 2.65625.$$

   We notice that the 1.6 has only two significant figures so that our answer should be limited to two significant figures giving us 2.7 (rounding up since the third number is 5 and numbers that are 5 and above are rounded up).

   Now for the powers of ten terms, we have

   $10^{-6} \times 10^{-4} / 10^{-5} = 10^{-6} \times 10^{-4} \times 10^5$

   And for the powers of ten we now add them $-6 + (-4) + 5 = -5$

   Thus our powers of ten are 10^{-5}.

   Combining the two terms gives us for the answer 2.7×10^{-5}

8. How many centimeters are in 45 meters?

   We know that there are 100 cm in one m or 10^{-2} m $= 1$ cm

   $$45 \text{ m} \times \frac{100 \text{ cm}}{1 \text{ m}} = 45 \times 100 \text{ m} = 4500 \text{ m} = 4.5 \times 10^3 \text{ m}$$

9. What is 6×10^{-6} divided by 3×10^{-2}?

   $$2 \times 10^{-4}$$

10. How many 250 mg pills can be made from 200 grams?

    First, change g to mg

    $200 \text{ g} \times 10^3 \text{ mg/g} = 200 \times 10^3 \text{ mg} = 2 \times 10^5 \text{ mg}$

    Now use the proportion approach giving

    $$\frac{1 \text{ pill}}{X \text{ pills}} = \frac{250 \text{ mg}}{2 \times 10^5 \text{ mg}}$$

    X pills $= 2 \times 10^5 / 250 = 800$ pills

11. A block that is blue colored and some what soft takes 2 kjoules to move up a hill; how many kjoules will it take to move 20 blocks of the same size up the same hill? The hill is 30 degrees and 200 meters long.

    Forget the blue and soft comments and for the time being that the hill is 30 degrees and 200 meters long since you are moving the blocks up the same hill so its length and elevation are held constant. Again, let us approach this as being solvable using the proportion approach.

    We can phrase the problem as follows-if it takes 2 kJ to move 1 block, how many kJ will it take to move 20 blocks?

$$\frac{2 \text{ kJ}}{X \text{ kJ}} = \frac{1 \text{ Block}}{20 \text{ Blocks}}$$

    Cross multiplication and solving for X gives

    X kJ = 20 × 2 = 40 kJ

12. Give a solution map for converting kg to mg.

$$kg \rightarrow g \rightarrow mg$$

13. What is 4.00×10^6 times 2.00×10^{-3} divided by 1.0×10^4 written in scientific notation with two significant figures?

    Again, separating out the term types gives us

    4.00 × 2.00/1.0 = 8.0 to two significant figures.

    The powers of ten are then

    $10^6 \times 10^{-3}/10^4 = 10^6 \times 10^{-3} \times 10^{-4}$

    6 + (−3) + (−4) = 6 − 3 − 4 = −1

    The answer is then 8.0×10^{-1}

14. How many significant figures are in the following?

    0.003470   4-all figures including the "0" are significant once non-zero figures start.

    7500   Don't know because of the absence of a ".".

    3.450×10^3 4-all figures, including zeros, are significant in scientific notation.

15. What is the mass of a rock whose density is 4 g/ml if it occupies a volume of 200 cc?

    Remember that the units cc, cm^3, and mL are the same.

    D = M/V when rearranged gives

    M = DV = 4 g/mL × 200 mL = 800 g.

16. A swimming pool was filled with water. It holds 1×10^8 mL. How many kiloliters is this?

    We know that 1,000 mL or 10^3 mL = 1 L and that 1,000 L or 10^3 L = 1 kL AND that

    10^{-3} L = 1 mL and 10^{-3} L = 1 kL

    Our short road map is

$$mL \rightarrow L \rightarrow kL$$

    1×10^8 mL × 10^{-3} L/mL × 10^{-3} kL/L = 1×10^2 kL

17. What are the basic SI units for weight, length, and volume?

   weight= grams

   length = meters

   volume= liters

18. Work is often measured in joules. How many kilojoules is needed to pick 20 bushels of weeds if it takes 3 millijoules to pick one bushel of weeds?

   First, we need to convert kJ to mJ or mJ to kJ. Let us concert mJ to kJ since our answer will need to be in kJ. Our fast road map is then

   $$mJ \rightarrow J \rightarrow kJ$$

   We know that 10^3 mJ = 1 J and 10^3 J = 1 kJ and we know 10^{-3} kJ = 1 J and 10^{-3} J = 1 mJ

   $$3 \text{ mJ} \times \frac{10^{-3} \text{ J}}{1 \text{ mJ}} \times \frac{10^{-3} \text{ kJ}}{1 \text{J}} = 3 \times 10^{-6} \text{ kJ}$$

   Now we can use our proportion approach again.

   $$\frac{3 \times 10^6 \text{ kJ}}{X \text{ kJ}} = \frac{1 \text{ Bushel}}{20 \text{ Bushels}}$$

   and X = $20 \times 3 \times 10^{-6} = 60 \times 10^{-6} = 6 \times 10^{-5}$ kJ

19. The radioactivity of a rock is 8,000 counts per seconds. How many counts is this per hour?

   We have memorized the "time" relationships just by our usage. We can develop a short road map seconds → minutes → hours

   and the relationships 60 secs = 1 min and 60 mins = 1 hr.

   8,000 counts/second × 60 secs/min × 60 mins/hr = 2.88×10^7 counts/hour

20. A car is traveling 60 kilometers per hour. How many centimeters per second is this?

   Again another conversion problem but here we have two items to convert. Let us combine the steps again in a road map that tells us which steps need to be done and in what order. We will start with the distance and then do the time portion giving us the following road map.

   $$km \rightarrow m \rightarrow cm \rightarrow hour \rightarrow minutes \rightarrow seconds$$

   $$60 \text{ km/hr} \times \frac{1000 \text{ m}}{1 \text{ km}} \times \frac{100 \text{ cm}}{1 m} \times \frac{1 \text{ hr}}{60 \text{ mins}} \times \frac{1 \text{ min}}{60 \text{ secs}} = 1.7 \times 10^3 \text{ cm/seconds}$$

21. A car is traveling at 100 kilometers/hour is traveling at _____ millimeters/second.

   As above, we will need to convert two both distance and time. Our combined road map is

   $$km \rightarrow m \rightarrow mm \rightarrow hours \rightarrow minutes \rightarrow seconds$$

   100 km/hr × 1000 m/km × 100 cm/m ×1 hr/ 60 minutes × 1 minute /60 seconds = 0.28×10^4 mm/sec = 2.8×10^3 mm/sec to two significant figures.

22. If the weight of one molecule of a material is 1.8×10^{-20} grams what is the weight of 6×10^{23} of this molecule?

Here we will again employ the proportion approach.

If one molecule weights 1.8×10^{-20} grams then 6×10^{23} molecules will weight how many grams.

$$\frac{1 \text{ molecule}}{6 \times 10^{23} \text{ molecules}} = \frac{1.8 \times 10^{-20} \text{ g}}{X \text{ g}}$$

Solving for $X = 1.8 \times 10^{-20} \text{g} \times 6 \times 10^{23} = 10.8 \times 10^3 \text{ g} = 1.08 \times 10^4 \text{g}$

23. For the above molecule, what is the weight of one molecule in kilograms?

   1 molecule weights 1.8×10^{-20} g $\times$ 1 g/1000 kg $= 1.8 \times 10^{-23}$ g

24. How many milligrams are in 2 kilograms?

   Again a brief road map is kg $\rightarrow$ g $\rightarrow$ mg

   2 kg $\times$ 1000 g/kg $\times$ 1000 mg/g $= 2 \times 10^6$ mg

25. How many nanograms are in 50 grams?

   The appropriate relationship that you should know it 10^9 ng $= 1$ g or 10^{-9} g $= 1$ ng.

   50 g $\times 10^9$ ng/g $= 50 \times 10^9$ ng $= 5 \times 10^{10}$ ng.

   Please note that in each of these conversion problems the conversion unit used allows for the non-wanted units to be cancelled.

26. How many significant figures are there in the number 3,402?

   4 significant figures since internal zeros are counted.

27. How many significant figures are there in the number 0.000003004?

   4 significant figures since internal zeros are counted and zeros that appear before non-zeros begin are not significant figures.

28. What is the density of air where 22,400 mL weights 4 grams? Give the answer to one significant figure in scientific notation.

   D = M/V = 4 g/22,400 mL = 0.000178571 g/mL and to two significant figures it is 0.00018 and in scientific notation it is 1.8×10^{-4} g/mL which is 2×10^{-4} g/mL to one significant figure. While this is a small number for liquids and solids, it is a typical number for gases.

29. What is the answer to the problem 2.02×10^6 times 4.0×10^{-4} and this divided by 3.000×10^{16}? How many significant figures should the answer contain?

   Again, separation of the two number groups gives $2.02 \times 4.0 / 3.000 = 2.693333333 = 2.7$ since the number of significant figures for the least accurately number 4.0 has two significant figures.

   For the powers of ten we have $10^6 \times 10^{-4} / 10^{16} = 10^6 \times 10^{-4} \times 10^{-16}$

   And $6 + (-4) + (-16) = 6 - 4 - 16 = -14$

   Combining we get 2.7×10^{-14}

30. What is 3.02×10^{-3} squared? What kind of unit might this be if the value is given as 3.02×10^{-3} inches and you are asked to square it? Volume, length, area.

   $9.1204 \times 10^{-6} = 9.12 \times 10^{-6}$ using three significant figures because the original number was given to only 3 significant numbers.

If the original unit was inches, squaring it would be inches squared, inches^2 which is an area.

If the number was cubed then the unit would be inches^3 which is a volume.

31. A rock displaces 13 mL of ethylene glycol and weights 4.03 grams. What is its density?

    D = M/V = 4.03 g /13 mL = 0.31 g/mL which indicates that the rock is light, probably some sort of pumas with lots of cavities.

32. What is the weight of a rock whose volume is 35 cc and whose density is 7.2 g/mL?

    First, since the units for density and volume are the same if we remember that 35 cc is also 35 mL.

    D = M/V Rearrangement gives M = DV. You can check to see if this is correct by using unit analysis. The appropriate units for both sides of the equation are

    g = g/mL × mL = g so the units on both sides of the equation are the same giving confidence that our expression is correct.

    M = DV = 7.2 g/mL × 35 mL = 252 g = 2.52 × 10^2 g = 2.5 × 10^2 g to two significant numbers.

SAMPLE TEST PROBLEMS

Name _____   **Date** _____

Circle only correct answers.

33. What is 6×10^4 times 3×10^{-7} divided by 9×10^7?

a. 2×10^4; b. 162×10^4; c. 2×10^{-10}; d. 4.5×10^{-18} e. 2×10^{-4}

34. What is 2×10^3 cubed?

a. 4×10^9; b. 4×10^6; c. 8×10^9; d. 6×10^6; e. 4×10^{12}

35. What is the weight of a rock with a density of 4 g/mL and a volume of 12 mL?

a. 48 mL; b. 3.3 mL; c. 48 g; d. 3.3 g; e. 3 g

36. How many significant figures does 0.0034500 have?

a. 1; b. 7; c. 5; d. 8; e. 3

37. How many significant figures does 5300 have?

a. 2; b. 4; c. don't know; d. 1; e. 3

38. Write 213 mg in scientific notation.

a. 213; b. 2.13×10^1; c. 2.13×10^2; d. 21.3×10^2; e. 2.13×10^{-2}

39. How many kilograms are in 30 grams?

a. 33 kg; b. 330 kg; c. 3×10^{-2} kg; d. 3×10^1 kg; e. 3000

40. What is the basic SI unit for volume?

a. milliliter; b. kilograms; c. liter; d. grams; e. seconds

41. What is the basic formula for density?

a. D = M/V; b. $E = mc^2$; c. Time = seconds × 60; d. D = M × V;
e. V = D × V.

42. There are about 120,000 people living in Coral Springs. What is this written in scientific notation to two significant figures?

a. 1.2×10^5; b. 12×10^4; c. 1.20×10^4 d. 12×10^5; e. 0.12×10^3.

43. What is 0.00004500 meters (m) written in scientific notation with 4 significant figures?

a. 4.500×10^{-8} m; b. 4.500×10^{-5}; c. 4.50×10^{-6};
d. 4.50000×10^{-5}; e. 4.500 m

44. What is 2.0×10^{-10} meters (m) multiplied by 6,000,000 in scientific notation given to 2 significant figures?

a. 3.33×10^{-12} m; b. 1.2×10^{11} m; c. 12.0×10^{-4} m;
d. 1.2×10^{-3} m; e. 120 m

45. What is the density of 300,000 mL of a gas that weights 4.00×10^{-4} grams? Write the answer in scientific notation with 2 significant figures and in density units of g/mL. The gas is green colored and very toxic.

a. 1.3 g/L; b. 7.50×10^6; c. 7.5×10^6; d. 1.3×10^{-9}; e. 1.3×10^{-4}.

46. A pill is oblong and pink colored. It is used to treat pimples. A 500 mg pill has ___ kilograms in it. Give the answer in scientific notation. It has a density of 3.2 g/mL.

    a. 5.0×10^4; b. 4×10^4; c. 5.0×10^{-8}; d. 5.0×10^{-4}; e. 1.3×10^{-4}.

47. A drug manufacture synthesized 500 kg of a new drug. How many 250 mg pills can they make (maximum) from the 500 kg of the new drug?

    a. 2.0×10^6; b. 5.0×10^8; c. 4×10^4; d. 2.5×10^{-8}; e. $2. \times 10^4$.

48. A 4 liter flask is intended to hold about _____ mL.

    a. 4; b. 400; c. 4,000; d. 40,000; e. 0.004.

49. The approximate population of California is about 38, 572,000. Express this in scientific notation to the nearest 100,000.

    a. 3.8×10^5; b. 3.857×10^6; c. 3.83; d. 3.85×10^6; d. 3.86×10^7; e. 3.85×10^8.

50. If the density of a round rock is 10 g/mL, what is the weight of this rock that displaces 150 mL of water?

    a. 15 mL; b. 1.5 kg; c. 1.5 L; d. 1.5 g; e. 0.67 g.

51. If it takes 3.0×10^{-3} kJ (kilojoules) of energy to hike 5 miles on a hot dry day, how many joules is this?

    a. 3; b. 2.0×10^6; c. 6×10^{-4}; d. 1.5×10^{-9}; e. 15.

52. What is 4.0×10^{-3} cubed? What kind of unit might this be?

    a. area, 2.0; b. volume, 4×10^6; c. length, 2.0×10^{-9}; d. volume, 6.4×10^{-8}; e. volume, 6.4×10^{-6}.

53. A 4.0 liter flask holds ____ mL.

    a. 4.0×10^{-8}; b. 4.0×10^3; c. 400; d. 4.0×10^6; e. 4.0×10^{-6}.

54. What is 6.0×10^{23} divided by 2.0×10^{-6}?

    a. 3.0×10^{-29}; b. 3.0×10^{29}; c. 3.0; d. 3.0×10^{31}; e. 3.0×10^{-12}.

55. How many significant figures is in the following distance written in scientific notation? 4.120×10^{-5} nm?

    a. 6; b. 3; c. 2; d. 5; e. 4.

56. What is $10^6 \times 10^{14} \times 10^{-7}$?

    a. 10^{27}; b. 10^{13}; c. 10^{-13}; d. 10^{15}; e. 10^{20}.

57. How many significant figures does 0.00003000200 have?

    a. 5; b. 6; c. 7; d. 8; e. 11?

58. Convert 2.34 kg to grams.

    a. 2.34×10^3; b. 23.4×10^{10}; c. 2.34×10^{-3}; d. 2.34×10^6; e. 2.34×10^{-4}.

59. The length of a certain type of cell is about 2.0×10^{-2} nm. What is the approximate distance of 4,000,000 laid end-to-end?

    a. 2.0×10^9 nm; b. 8×10^4 nm; c. 8 nm; d. 8.0×10^{-8} nm e. 8.0×10^6 nm.

60. What is 20350 nanometers written in scientific notation to 4 significant figures?

a. 2.035; b. 2.035×10^4; c. 2.035×10^5; d. 2.035×10^{-4} ; e. 2.035×10^{-6}.

61. There are _____ kg in 4,000 g.

a. 400; b. 4,000; c. 40; d. 4; e. 0.4.

62. Four arrows are shot into a target and all four hit the bulls-eye. This is high _____ and high _____.

a. significance and aromaticity; b. precision and basics; c. precision and accuracy; d. conversion and sorting; e. conception and basics.

63. The population of Parkland, FL is about 102,000. Write this in scientific notation such that it shows confidence to the nearest thousand.

a. 1.02×10^4; b. 10.2×10^4; c. 1.02×10^5; d. 102×10^3; e. 102.

64. What is $10^3 \times 10^{-13} \times 10^{15} \times 10^{-8}$?

a. 10^{-3}; b. 10^{26}; c. 10^{-13}; d. 10^{-39}; e. 10^3.

65. What is $10^{15} \times 10^{-7} \times 10^{16}$ divided by $10^{16} \times 10^{-3}$?

a. 10^{57}; b. 10^{11}; c. 10^9; d. 10^{-11}; e. 10^{-9}.

Matter and Change

CLASSIFICATION OF MATTER

Let us again review some of the material given in Section 1. Matter can be classified as pure matter and mixtures and further divided as below. We need to be able to read such charts and relationships to see how the individual entries are related.

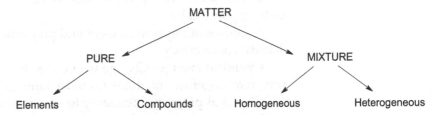

What is an **element**? An element is matter that has only one kind of atom. It can be monoatomic or diatomic or more.

What is a **compound**? A compound has more than one kind of atom in it.

What is a **mixture**? Has more than one kind of matter in it.

What is a **homogeneous mixture**? Mixture of compounds and/or elements that are in the same phase. Mixture appears to be homogeneous or the same throughout.

What is a **heterogeneous mixture**? Mixture of compounds and/or elements that are separated from one another. The mixture appears to be heterogeneous or unlike throughout.

While they are different, we will use mass (caused by weight of atoms) and weight (gravitational force) interchangeably.

MATTER-what occupies space and can be perceived by us

MASS-quantity of matter in a material

WEIGHT-force of gravity

PHASES

Matter can also be divided according to being solid, liquid or gas. Solids, liquids and gases are called states of matter or **phases**. The volume of a material is the amount of space taken up by the material. The three major states of matter or phases are

Solids have a fixed or definite volume and shape. They are rigid and generally have the highest density of the three main phases.

Liquids have a definite volume and occupy the shape of the container but do not always fill the container. Liquids are relatively incompressible.

Gases occupy the entire volume of the container with no fixed shape and they are easily compressed.

In general, gas molecules are far apart and travel rapidly, many average about 1,000 miles/hour in speed.

CHEMICAL AND PHYSICAL CHANGES

Physical change- Change in form of matter but not chemical identity-melting, boiling.

Physical property- Characteristic observed for a material without changing its chemical identity.

EXTENSIVE PROPERTY-magnitude depends on amount of material-mass and volume.

INTENSIVE PROPERTY-independent of amount of material-density, melting point, color.

Examples of physical changes and properties are melting, boiling, color, density, conductivity.

Chemical change- Change where the atoms are arranged in a different way; rearrangement of atoms from reactants to products.

Chemical property - Tendency to rearrange atoms in a chemical reaction

Example of chemical changes/properties are iron rusting; reaction between hydrogen and oxygen forming water; tendency of sodium to react with the moisture in the air forming eventually sodium hydroxide.

We cannot create more matter nor can we lose matter in our ordinary chemical reactions. In nuclear energy we can create lots of energy through the transformation of mass into energy according to Einstein's famous relationship $E = mc^2$.

TEMPERATURE SCALES

We have three temperature scales we should be aware of. These are all given names of people. The Fahrenheit is the temperature scale we use. But in science we use the Kelvin and Celsius scales so we should be aware of them. In particular, we should be aware that the freezing point of water is

0 C = 273 K = 32 F and that the boiling point of water is

100 C = 373 K = 212 F

We should also be aware that at zero degrees Kelvin; −273 °C and −459 °F that all motion stops. This is referred to as absolute zero. We cannot go lower than this.

ENERGY AND CHEMICAL AND PHYSICAL CHANGE

PHYSICAL CHANGE

As materials move from one phase to another there are energy changes. Also, as we heat up a material it takes energy to increase its temperature AND as we cool a material energy is given up.

Thus, as we heat up ice (water in the solid form) from −20 C to 0 C it takes energy. At 0 C the ice has sufficient energy to allow conversion into liquid water, that is the ice melts. We continue to add energy until all of the solid water has become liquid water. This phase transition from solid ice to liquid water is called melting. We can add energy to the liquid heating the water eventually to 100 C where we again have sufficient energy to convert the water to another phase. The liquid water can now be changed to vapor or gaseous water or steam. It takes a lot of energy to achieve this phase change from liquid to vapor. This phase transition is called boiling. After all of the liquid water is changed to steam or the vapor state we again add energy and increase the temperature of the vapor.

While there are many forms of energy, here we will look at heat energy which is measured by temperature. Thus, as the temperature of a material is increased energy is added and as the temperature of a material is decreased energy is given off.

We measure the amount of energy to increase the temperature of materials. The **heat capacity** is the amount of energy (usually in joules) required to change the temperature of a material by one degree Celsius, 1 °C or here simply 1 C. When this amount of heat is redefined as the amount of energy required to change the temperature of **one gram** of material 1 C it is called **specific heat capacity** or simply **specific heat**. The units of specific heat are J/g C or sometimes written as J/g-C or in words joules per gram per Celsius degree.

We can rewrite this in terms of

Amount of heat (or simply heat) = mass × specific heat × temperature change or

$$q = m \times C \times \Delta T$$

Question: Given that the heat capacity of water is 4 J/g-C how much energy is needed to heat 500 g of water 20 C?

$$q = 500 \text{ g} \times 4 \text{ J/g-C} \times 20 \text{ C} = 40{,}000 \text{ J or } 40 \text{ kJ (note that } 1{,}000 \text{ J} = 1 \text{ kJ)}$$

Note how the units cancel.

There are many different ways similar problems can be given.

Question: Given that the heat capacity of water is 4 J/g-C, how much energy is needed to heat 750 mL of water from 40 to 55 C?

We are given the same information as in the prior problem but we need to remember several things.

First, for water since the density of water is 1 g/mL the number of mL of water is equal to the number of grams. Thus, 750 mL = 750 g.

Next, rather than directly giving the temperature change, it is given in terms of a starting temperature, 40 C, and final temperature, 55. The temperature difference is 55 − 40 = 15 C.

Now we have the information in the correct form to use our general equation.

$$q \text{ (joules)} = 750 \text{ g} \times 4 \text{ J/g/C} \times 15 \text{ C} = 45{,}000 \text{ J or } 45 \text{ kJ.}$$

We can also use this approach to determine any one of the factors, q, m, heat capacity, temperature difference, given the other values.

Question: What is the heat capacity of a material if it takes 20,000 J of energy to heat 8 grams of the material 12 C? Let us first modify the equation by solving for heat capacity.

$$q = m \times \text{heat capacity} \times \Delta T$$

Divide both sides by m $\times$ Δ T giving

q / (m $\times$ Δ T) = heat capacity

Now we will place in the given values.

20,000 J / (8 g $\times$ 12 C) = 1,000 J or 1 kJ

ENDOTHERMIC AND EXOTHERMIC CHANGES

An endothermic change can be physical or chemical. The energy change in endothermic changes is such that a net amount of energy is taken on. We have an endoskeleton with our bones fitted inside our skin. The melting of an ice cube is endothermic so when you hold an ice cube in your hand, your hand feel cool since energy is being taken from the surroundings, including your hand, to melt the ice cube. The reaction between nitrogen and oxygen forming nitrogen monooxide is endothermic and the surroundings supply energy to the reaction.

By comparison, exothermic changes give off a net amount of energy. Insects have an exoskeleton. The reaction between hydrogen and oxygen forms water and lots of energy which we find in the form of heat.

Chemical reactions can give up a net amount of energy or take on a net amount of energy. Those reactions that given up energy are called **exothermic** reactions and those that take on energy are called **endothermic** reactions.

Matter changes phase with temperature and pressure. Generally, materials move from solid to liquid to gas as temperature increases. Here we will look at only temperature influences (Figure 3.1). Let's start with a cube of ice. It is cold, sufficiently cold so the individual water molecules are locked in place with little movement. As we raise the temperature, we reach a temperature where there is sufficient energy available as heat energy to allow the water molecules to break away from the solid lattice and begin wholesale movement. This point is called the **melting point** and the process is called **melting**. As we increase the temperature we continually add heat energy to the melted ice cube until we have sufficient energy present that allows the liquid water molecules to be ripped from the liquid phase into the gaseous phase. This temperature is called the **boiling point** and the phase change is called **evaporation**.

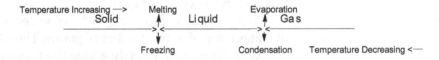

Figure 3.1 *Phases and phase changes as a function of temperature.*

Conversely, we can reduce the thermal energy of vapor water molecules so that they **condense** becoming liquid and as the thermal energy, temperature, is further reduced the liquid water molecules become frozen (**freezing**).

To melt our ice cube takes energy and the same amount of energy is released, given back, when the liquid water returns to the solid, frozen state. Like-wise, the energy required to heat liquid water to become vapor or gaseous water is the same amount of energy released, given back, when the same amount of vapor condenses giving liquid water (Figure 3.2).

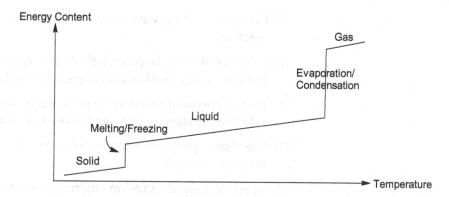

Figure 3.2 *Energy content of water as a function of temperature.*

COMPOSITION OF MATTER

Matter, solid, liquid and gas, can be classified according to their composition. **Elements** are materials that contain only one kind of atom. Thus, iron, aluminum and copper are elements. Some elements come in groups. For instance, hydrogen, oxygen, nitrogen, and the halogens all come in groups of two. Each molecule of these elements naturally have two atoms of that element in them. **Compounds** are materials that contain more than one kind of element. thus, common table salt is sodium chloride having sodium and chlorine combined. Water has hydrogen and oxygen combined. Both sodium chloride and water are compounds because they have more than one element in them.

Matter can be classified according to purity. A **pure material** has only that material in it. Thus, a gold ring should have only gold atoms in it. Whereas a white gold ring is an alloy containing a "white" metal such as nickel, manganese, or palladium. Thus, the white gold ring is not pure gold but rather is a mixture. A **mixture** contains different kinds of atoms. This mixture may be **homogeneous** such as the gases in the air we breathe, or may be **heterogeneous** as are most salad dressings.

PROBLEMS

1. What are the three usual states of matter?

2. What is a pure substance?

3. What are some properties of a gas?

4. What are some properties of a solid and give some examples of materials that are solid at room temperature?

5. What is the difference between a mixture and a compound?

6. What is the difference between a compound and an element?

7. Is a Mars candy bar a pure material or a mixture?

8. Water and gasoline are not soluble in one another so when mixed together they form _____ phases and are said to be _____.

9. Gasoline reacting with oxygen to run a car is an example of a _____ reaction.

10. Rubbing alcohol, isopropyl alcohol, evaporates relatively rapidly from the skin giving the skin a cooling sensation. What kind of reaction is this?

11. Does a chemical reaction occur when a copper coin is dropped into a solution containing nitric acid and a blue solution results?

12. Gasoline rapidly evaporates when poured onto the ground. Is this a physical change?

13. In an internal combustion engine gasoline is converted into carbon dioxide and water. Is this a chemical reaction and if so why?

14. In general we find that the burning of compounds that contain only carbon and hydrogen, called hydrocarbons, form carbon dioxide and water. Where does the oxygen come from since hydrocarbons contains only hydrogen and carbon and yet water contains oxygen?

15. Natural gas is almost totally methane which is a hydrocarbon. What are the main products you expect from burning methane?

16. Our swimming pools contain mostly water in them but also some dissolved gases and chlorine. What kind of mixture is our pool?

17. Which of the following is a compound? common table salt, NaCl; Sugar, $C_6H_{12}O_6$; oxygen, O_2.

18. We eat food that is converted eventually into energy through a complex of changes. Are these changes chemical changes?

19. What temperature does water boil and freeze in the Fahrenheit scale.

20. What temperature does water boil and freeze in the Celsius temperature scale.

21. Which picture below best depicts NH_3 as a gas?

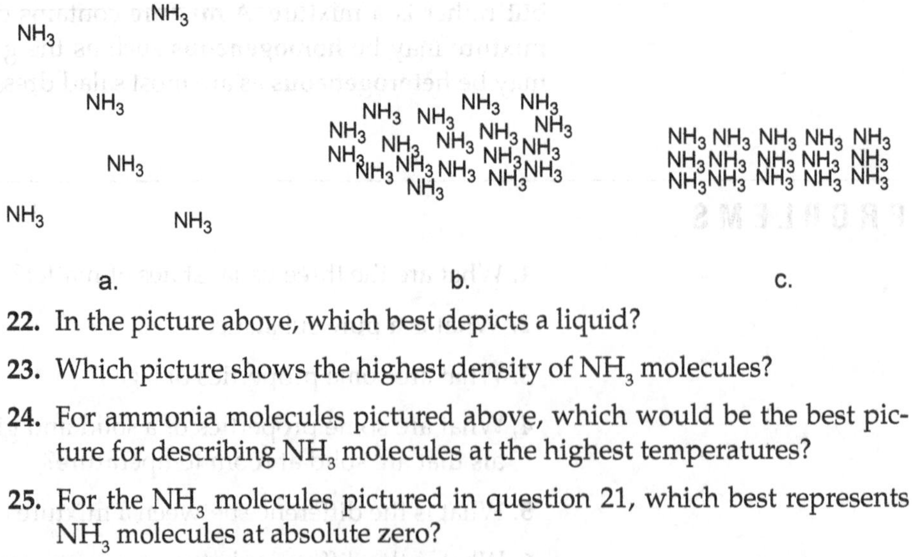

a.   b.   c.

22. In the picture above, which best depicts a liquid?

23. Which picture shows the highest density of NH_3 molecules?

24. For ammonia molecules pictured above, which would be the best picture for describing NH_3 molecules at the highest temperatures?

25. For the NH_3 molecules pictured in question 21, which best represents NH_3 molecules at absolute zero?

26. Is NH_3 a compound or element? Why?

27. The air we breathe is composed of about 20% oxygen, 70% nitrogen and the remaining a mixture of other gases. It is a _____ mixture. Which picture below is the most reasonable representation of our air?

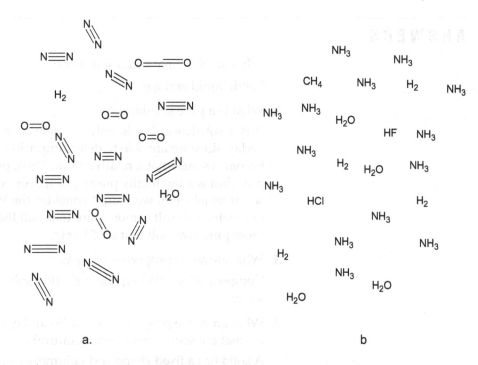

a.   b

28. For the picture shown in question 27, which picture has the greatest density of compounds?

29. Which of the following is a homogeneous mixture? wine with particulates, chocolate chip cookies, coffee with grounds, gasoline

30. What is the difference between a homogeneous mixture and a pure compound?

31. Which of the following is not a chemical property?

    Density   Color   Reactivity with water
    Refractive index   solubility in water
    Forms hydroxides with water

32. The formation of ice from water is a(an) _____ process.

33. Which of the following is a chemical change? Why?

    A. Iron and chromium solder melts when heated and is used to make stain glass windows. After melting it cools connecting the pieces of glass.

    B. Nitrogen in the atmosphere when struck by lightning reacts with oxygen, also in the air, forming nitrogen oxides.

    C. Nitrogen and hydrogen in the air can form ammonia, NH_3, thereby fixing the nitrogen.

    D. When cooled sufficiently carbon dioxide gas forms a solid called dry ice. It is called dry ice because it is cold and evaporates directly from the solid to a gas. It is used to make fog in pictures and on stage by addition of some water to the dry ice. The water forms a mist like fog.

34. One kind of hand warmer uses the reaction between oxygen and iron power forming iron oxides and energy in the form of heat. What kind of reaction is this?

35. Give some properties of a liquid.

ANSWERS

1. What are the three usual states of matter?

Solid, liquid and gas

2. What is a pure substance?

It is a substance that is only a single material-compound or element. Today, since we are able to detect impurities to such low amounts, pure becomes somewhat a relative term. Thus, pure table salt can be 99.99% pure, but is it not totally pure since it does contain 0.01% impurity. Even so, in usual cases we would consider the 99.9% pure salt as pure. We know that this salt is more pure than salt that is only 99% pure which is more pure than salt that is 95%, etc.

3. What are some properties of a gas?

Compressible, traveling relatively (to a solid) fast, is dilute, lots of vacant space.

4. What are some properties of a solid and give some examples of materials that are solid at room temperature?

A solid has a fixed shape and volume; rock, wood, plastic handle, etc.

5. What is the difference between a mixture and a compound?

A compound has groups of atoms that are combined in the same proportions such as water molecules all have two hydrogen atoms and one oxygen atom. A mixture is composed of more than one compound and/ or element.

6. What is the difference between a compound and an element?

Compounds have more than one kind of atom; composed of more than one element; elements have only one kind of atom and can be present in groups of one such as argon, neon, and groups of two molecular oxygen, hydrogen, chlorine, and groups of four as phosphorus and in groups of eight as in the case of sulfur.

7. Is a Mars candy bar a pure material or a mixture?

Mars bars contains lots of different materials so it is a mixture.

8. Water and gasoline are not soluble in one another so when mixed together they form _____ phases and are said to be _____.

Two phases and are said to be immiscible.

9. Gasoline reacting with oxygen to run a car is an example of a _____ reaction.

Chemical or exothermic

10. Rubbing alcohol, isopropyl alcohol, evaporates relatively rapidly from the skin giving the skin a cooling sensation. What kind of reaction is this?

Endothermic or physical. In many of these where there can be several "correct" answers. A good way to see which of the several possible correct answers can be gleamed from looking to see what the possible answers are. Typically there is only one correct answers unless one of the answers has more than one of the correct answers included in it.

11. Does a chemical reaction occur when a copper coin is dropped into a solution containing nitric acid and a blue solution results?

Yes, the formation of the blue color is evidence that something chemical occurred since neither the copper coin or nitric acid solution are colored.

12. Gasoline rapidly evaporates when poured onto the ground. Is this a physical change?

    Yes, since the gasoline is simply evaporating and not forming a new compound.

13. In an internal combustion engine gasoline is converted into carbon dioxide and water. Is this a chemical reaction and if so why?

    It is a chemical reaction because the gasoline is converted into another compounds through rearrangement of the chemical atoms and reaction with oxygen.

14. In general we find that the burning of compounds that contain only carbon and hydrogen, called hydrocarbons, form carbon dioxide and water. Where does the oxygen come from since hydrocarbons contains only hydrogen and carbon and yet water contains oxygen?

    The oxygen comes from our atmosphere. The air we take in has about 20% oxygen in it.

15. Natural gas is almost totally methane which is a hydrocarbon. What are the main products you expect from burning methane?

    Since it is a hydrocarbon mainly carbon dioxide and water are produced.

16. Our swimming pools contain mostly water in them but also some dissolved gases and chlorine. What kind of mixture is our pool?

    Homogeneous mixture.

17. Which of the following is a compound? Common table salt, NaCl; Sugar, $C_6H_{12}O_6$; oxygen, O_2.

    Only oxygen is not a compound since it contains only oxygen atoms.

18. We eat food that is converted eventually into energy through a complex of changes. Are these changes chemical changes?

    Yes. Almost each of the steps going from food to energy involves changes in the chemical structure of the products and reactants.

19. What temperature does water boil and freeze in the Fahrenheit scale.

    Water boils about 212 F and freezes at 32 F.

20. What temperature does water boil and freeze in the Celsius temperature scale.

    Water boils at 100 C and freezes at 0 C.

21. Which picture below best depicts NH_3 as a gas?

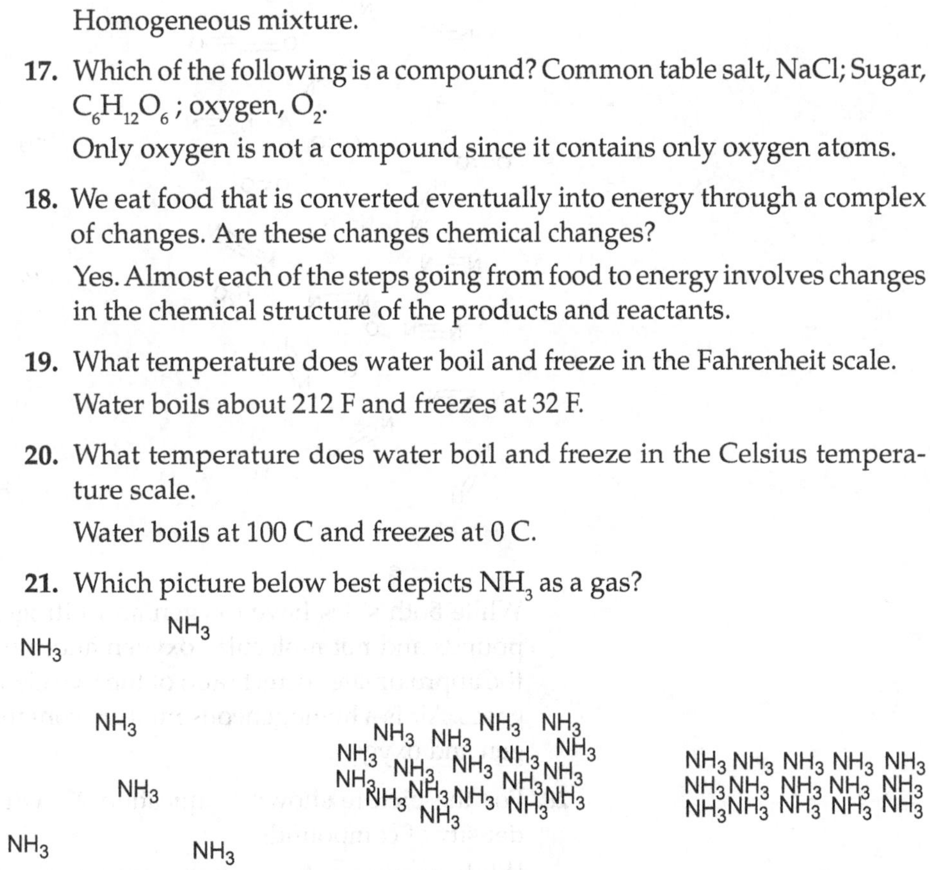

NH_3
NH_3

NH_3

NH_3

NH_3 NH_3

NH_3 NH_3 NH_3 NH_3
NH_3 NH_3 NH_3 NH_3 NH_3
NH_3 NH_3 NH_3 NH_3 NH_3
NH_3 NH_3 NH_3 NH_3
NH_3

NH_3 NH_3 NH_3 NH_3 NH_3
NH_3 NH_3 NH_3 NH_3 NH_3
NH_3 NH_3 NH_3 NH_3 NH_3

Picture "a" best depicts a gas since the molecules are far apart.

22. In the picture above, which best depicts a liquid?

Picture "b" since the NH_3 molecules are close together but not in a well-ordered array.

23. Which picture shows the highest density of NH_3 molecules?

Picture "c" shows the highest density of ammonia molecules with the most ammonia molecules fitted together in the least space.

24. For ammonia molecules pictured above, which would be the best picture for describing NH_3 molecules at the highest temperature?

As temperature increases, the energy available to move ammonia from a solid to a liquid to a gas increases, thus picture "a" best represents ammonia as a gas.

25. For the NH_3 molecules pictured in question 21, which best represents NH_3 molecules at absolute zero?

Absolute zero is the lowest temperature unattainable so the system will be as a solid so this is best pictured as "c".

26. Is NH_3 a compound or element? Why?

NH_3 is a compound since it contains two or more elements, hydrogen and nitrogen.

27. The air we breathe is composed of about 20% oxygen, 70% nitrogen and the remaining a mixture of other gases. It is a _____ mixture. Which picture below is the most reasonable representation of our air?

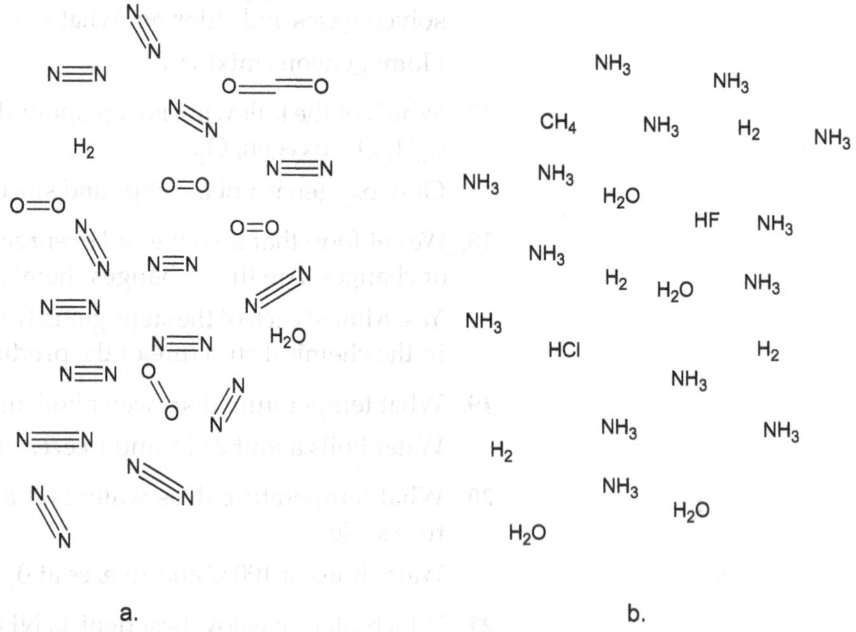

a.   b.

While both sides have oxygen and nitrogen, side b has them as compounds and not molecular oxygen and nitrogen whereas picture a has the approximate correct ratio of the two elements along with a few other gases. Air is a homogeneous mixture containing mostly elemental nitrogen and oxygen.

28. For the picture shown in question 27, which picture has the greatest density of compounds?

While picture a has a few compounds, picture b has almost only compounds.

29. Which of the following is a homogeneous mixture? wine with particulates, chocolate chip cookies, coffee with grounds, gasoline

Gasoline is the only one that is a homogeneous mixture.

30. What is the difference between a homogeneous mixture and a pure compound?

A pure compound has only one kind of molecule that is composed of two or more elements but a homogenous mixture has more than one compound and or element in it.

31. Which of the following is not a chemical property? We remember that a chemical property is a chemical property of a material such as a tendency to react with something.

Density-physical   Color-physical Reactivity with water-chemical
Refractive index-physical   solubility in water-physical
Forms hydroxides with water-chemical

32. The formation of ice from water is a _____ process.

There are several possible answers-exothermic and physical are two possible answers. We can look at the possible answers in the exam to see which is the correct answer for the exam question. For the exothermic answer we can think of it as a phase change from liquid to solid. To do this heat must be extracted so it can be rewritten as liquid goes to solid plus energy so a net amount of energy is given off-that is it is an exothermic process.

$$\text{water liquid} \rightarrow \text{ice} + \text{energy}$$

33. Which of the following is a chemical change? Why?

A. Iron and chromium solder melts when heated and is used to make stain glass windows. After melting it cools connecting the pieces of glass. It is a physical change since material did not change molecular structure.

B. Nitrogen in the atmosphere when struck by lightning reacts with oxygen, also in the air, forming nitrogen oxides. It is a chemical change since there was a rearrangement of atoms forming new compounds.

C. Nitrogen and hydrogen in the air can form ammonia, NH_3, thereby fixing the nitrogen. It is a chemical changed since atoms rearranged forming a new compound.

D. When cooled sufficiently carbon dioxide gas forms a solid called dry ice. It is called dry ice because it is cold and evaporates directly from the solid to a gas. It is used to make fog in pictures and on stage by addition of some water to the dry ice. The water forms a mist like fog. It is a physical change since there was no chemical rearrangement of elements forming new compounds.

34. One kind of hand warmer uses the reaction between oxygen and iron power forming iron oxides and energy in the form of heat. What kind of reaction is this?

It is an exothermic chemical reaction.

35. Give some properties of a liquid.

Fluid taking the shape of the container; relatively dense compared to gases.

SAMPLE TEST PROBLEMS

Name _____   **Date** _____

Circle only correct answers.

36. Which of the following is not a typical phase of matter?
a. solid; b. flexibility; c. liquid; d. gas.

37. Which of the following is a homogeneous mixture?
a. soil; b. air; c. water and gasoline; d. chocolate chip cookie;
e. salad dressing.

38. Which phase is described as having molecules moving rapidly with the molecules far apart from one another and the molecules filling the container.
a. solid; b. rubber; c. liquid; d. gas; e. ice cube.

39. Silicon dioxide is a name for sand. Silicon dioxide units are arranged in a somewhat disordered manner. This disordered manner is often referred to as being _____.
a. crystalline; b. plastic; c. liquid; d. random; e. amorphous.

40. Which of the following is NOT a compound?
a. water; b. sand, SiO_2; c. common table salt, NaCl; d. iron;
e. a sugar, $C_6H_{12}O_6$.

41. Which of the following is NOT a physical property of iron?
a. conducts electrical current; b. reacts with oxygen forming rust;
c. is silver colored; d. is dense; e. is a solid at room conditions.

42. Which of the following is a chemical property?
a. methane burns forming carbon dioxide and water; b. fingernail-polish evaporates leaving behind a solid coating; c. ice melts forming water; d. rug fades on constant exposure to sunlight; e. both a and d.

43. Gasoline burns giving a greater weight of carbon dioxide and water than the original weight of gasoline. Where does the increased weight come from?
a. impurities in the gasoline create more hydrocarbons that also burn;
b. in the combustion process, oxygen from the air accounts for the increased weight; c. gasoline reacts with the nitrogen in the air accounting for the increased weight; d. because of the heat created by the burning of the gasoline more weight is created.

44. Which is the greatest energy?
a. 5 kJ; b. 5 J; c. 5 mJ; d. 5 cJ; e. 5 nJ.

45. The reaction between hydrogen and oxygen forms lots of energy. It is said to be a(n) _____ reaction.
a. creative; b. combustion; c. exothermic; d. endothermic;
e. acid/base

46. Which of the following is not a property of a gas?
a. average speed is about 1,000 miles per hour; b. only small attraction between gas molecules; c. occupies the volume of the container;

d. average speed of gas molecules increase as temperature is increased;

e. has a fixed and finite shape.

47. There are about 120,000 people living in Coral Springs. What is this written in scientific notation to two significant figures?

a. 1.2×10^5;   b. 12×10^4;   c. 1.20×10^4 d. 12×10^5;   e. 0.12×10^3.

48. What is the phase change called when solid water (ice) is converted to liquid water?

a. freezing;   b. vaporization;   c. boiling;   d. sublimation;

e. melting.

49. Since energy is added to melt water, it is referred to as an _____ transition.

a. exothermic;   b. endothermic;   c. calorimetric;   d. jouleic;

e. activation.

50. What kind of matter or phase has molecules that travel about 1,000 miles/hour, has a low density, the molecules are relatively far apart, the volume is fixed by the container as is its shape.

a. funny;   b. liquid;   c. gas;   d. solid;   e. atom.

51. The gas that we breath is an example of what kind of matter?

a. compound;   b. homogeneous mixture;   c. pure substance;d. pure matter;   e. pure element.

52. Which of the following is an example of a chemical change or property?

a. iron having a boiling point in excess of 1000 C;   b. iron boiling;

c. iron rusting; d. iron has a density of about 5 g/mL;   e. iron is silver colored.

53. Which of the following is most probably a homogeneous mixture.

a. clean air;   b. concrete;   c. strawberry sundae;   d. rice pudding;

e. moose tracks ice cream.

54. Ethylene is both a ripening agent for bananas and the starting material for making polyethylene. Following are properties of ethylene. Which of the following is a chemical property?

a. odorless;   b. flammable;   c. gas at room temperature;   d. mixes well with butanol; e.   colorless.

55. Since essentially all combustions of hydrocarbons give off heat, what kind of reaction would be the combustion of gasoline to run our automobiles?

a. exothermic;   b. freezing;   c. endothermic;   d. hydrocarbon fractionation;   e. cooling.

Atoms and the Periodic Table

DALTON'S ATOMIC THEORY

Dalton's Atomic Theory served as a basic for modern chemistry. While most of the postulates are not quite right, it still serves as a reasonable starting place.

1. ALL matter is composed of indivisible atoms. Atoms retain their identity in chemical reactions.

$$2H_2 + O_2 \rightarrow 2H_2O$$

2. An element has only ONE kind of atom. Atoms of a given element are alike in mass and other chemical and physical properties. These properties are different from the precise properties of atoms of other elements.

3. Atoms of different elements and compounds combine forming new compound/element combinations. A compound is composed of atoms of more than one element chemically combined in fixed proportions. A CHEMICAL REACTION consists of a rearrangement of the atoms present in the reacting substance(s) to give a NEW chemical combination. Thus, water contains one oxygen atom and two hydrogen atoms.

Implied is that atoms are not created, destroyed, or changed into other elements in chemical reactions. So alchemy is out except in nuclear reactions.

STRUCTURE OF THE ATOM

Atoms are composed of three basic or fundamental particles. These particles are described as follows.

Name Symbol	Charge	Relative mass	Where located
ELECTRON e	negative one	1	about nucleus
PROTON p	positive one	1800	in nucleus
NEUTRON n	neutral	1800	in nucleus

As shown below, the massive protons and neutrons are contained within in central core called the nucleus while electrons exist around the nucleus.

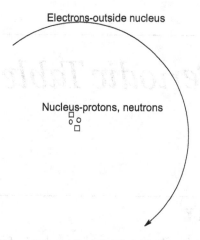

Electrons-outside nucleus

Nucleus-protons, neutrons

Nucleons- protons and neutrons.

We will learn that the number of protons determine what element the atom is. The periodic chart is arranged according to the number of protons within each kind of atom. This number is called the atomic number.

We will also learn that the formation of primary bonds occurs because of exchanges of and the sharing of electrons. Bonds formed from exchange of electrons are called ionic bonds and bonds formed from sharing electrons are called covalent bonds.

PROTONS DETERMINE THE ELEMENT

Atomic number- number of protons in the nucleus of an atom.

Mass number- total number of protons and neutrons in the nucleus of an atom.

Isotope- atoms of the SAME element that differ in the number of neutrons. Thus we have hydrogen with three isotopes- ALL have one proton, one has no neutrons, one has one neutron, and one has two neutrons.

The charge on each electron is given as a negative one. The charge on each proton is positive one. The charge on a neutron is zero. When we note the charge on an atom we consider the NET charge. Thus an atom with 8 electrons and 8 protons has a net charge of zero since the number of negative charges, electrons, is the same as the number of positive charges, protons. This atom is the oxygen atom since it has 8 protons and it is the NUMBER of PROTONS that determine which element it is.

We can show this as

$$
\begin{array}{r}
+8 \\
-8 \\
\hline
\text{net } 0
\end{array}
$$

The charge on an atom that has 8 protons and 10 electrons is a net minus two.

We can show this as

$$
\begin{array}{r}
+8 \\
-10 \\
\hline
\text{net } -2
\end{array}
$$

We can picture this as O^{-2}.

An element that has 17 protons, 18 electrons is Cl^{-1}. A neutral element that has 19 protons has 19 electrons is potassium, K. It is neutral because the number of protons and electrons is the same. If we have a neutral atom and two electrons are taken from it the charge on the atom is a net minus two because it now has two negatively charged "extra" electrons.

PATTERNS AND THE PERIODIC TABLE

As already noted, the periodic table is arranged according to the number of protons in an atom. Since the number of protons and number of electrons are the same in a neutral atom then when we know the number of protons and that the atom is neutral then we know the number of electrons.

The periodic table is a wonderful guide that allows us to express a lot of chemistry. There are two general types of bonding present in compounds. Bonding can occur through the loss and gain of electrons forming ionic compounds. In general, elements that are towards the left of the periodic table are called **metals** and they often give up electrons when they form compounds forming **ionic compounds**. Elements to the left of the periodic table have a greater tendency to pull electrons from the metals, the elements on the right of the periodic table, and are given the name **non-metals**. Many of the non-metals form compounds through sharing electrons forming **covalent bonds**. Notice that bonding involves electrons and later we will learn that the loss/gain and sharing involves electrons that are furthest from the central positive core or nucleus.

The elements are divided into vertical rows or columns which are called **families**. The first column containing elements such as sodium (Na) and potassium (K)), but not hydrogen (H), are called **alkaline metals** and when forming compounds take on a positive one charge because they give up on negatively charged electrons leaving the resulting atom deficient in one electron and it is said to be a plus one charge.

$$\text{Thus, for } Na \rightarrow Na^{+1} + e^{-1} \quad \text{or} \quad Na \rightarrow Na^{+} + e^{-}$$

The second column containing elements such as calcium (Ca) and barium (Ba) have the family name of **alkaline earths**. These metals generally give up two electrons when they form compounds so are said to become positively two charged.

$$\text{Thus, for } Ca \rightarrow Ca^{+2} + 2e^{-}$$

The third vertical column containing compounds such as aluminum (Al) and gallium (Ga) generally give up or lose three electrons when they form compounds.

$$\text{Thus, for } Al \rightarrow Al^{+3} + 3e^{-}$$

The next column of elements containing carbon (C) and silicon (Si) generally does not exchange electrons but rather form covalent bonds.

The next column of elements containing elements such as phosphorus (P) and arsenic (As) generally gain three electrons when they form ionic bonds.

$$P + 3e^{-} \rightarrow P^{-3}$$

The next column containing oxygen (O) and sulfur (S) generally gain two electrons when they form ionic compounds.

$$O + 2e^- \rightarrow O^{-2}$$

The next column that contains fluorine (F) and bromine (Br) are given the name **halogens**. These atoms generally take on a single electron when they form ionic compounds.

$$F + e^- \rightarrow F^-$$

Finally, the last column that contains helium (He) and argon (Ar) have a great tendency to not react, neither sharing or exchanging electrons. They are known by several names including **rare gases** or **noble gasses**.

We will discuss more of the periodic table later. Even so, as noted above members of the same family or vertical row tend to have the same valence number meaning they tend to add or lose the same number of electrons. This is shown below for main group elements.

Electrons Lost/Gained	+1	+2	+3	0	−3	−2	−1	0
	H							He
	Li	Be	B	C	N	O	F	Ne
	Na	Mg	Al	Si	P	S	Cl	Ar
	K	Ca	Ga	Ge	As	Se	Br	Kr
	Rb	Sr	In	Sn	Sb	Te	I	Xe
	Cs	Ba	Tl	Pb	Bi	Po	At	Rn

Thus, members of a single family all have the same number of valence electrons and will typically lose (becoming positively charged) or gain (becoming negatively charged) the same number of electrons.

When forming simple ionic compounds the typical charges taken by these elements allow us to predict the formula of the resulting compound. Thus, sodium chloride has a formula of NaCl since it is neutral and each Na is a plus one and each Cl is a negative one. Sodium oxide has a formula of Na_2O since it is neutral and each Na is a plus one but each oxygen is a negative two requiring two sodium atoms to neutralize the negative two oxygen charge.

$$Na^+ Cl^- \qquad 2Na^+ O^{-2}$$

As noted before, where there is a loss or gain of electrons, the resulting compounds are called **ionic compounds** and the associated bonds connecting the atoms are called **ionic bonds**. Atoms that have given up electrons becoming positively charged, such as Na^+ and Sr^{+2} are called **cations**. Atoms that take on electrons becoming negatively charged such as Br^{-1} and O^{-2} are called **anions**.

In general, those elements that tend to give up electrons, that is cations, are called metals and they occupy about 75% of the elements. Those elements that tend to take on electrons forming anions are called non-metals and they reside on the extreme right of the periodic table. The division between metals and non-metals is not clear but occurs in a stair-step fashion with B, Si, Ge, As, Sb, and Te being the stair-step elements, often called metalloid elements, between the metals and non-metals.

MASS NUMBER

The mass number is simply the number of nucleons or number of protons and neutrons. Thus, an oxygen atom with 9 protons has a mass number of 8 (because oxygen is element 8 meaning it has an atomic number of 8 meaning it has 8 protons) plus 9 or 17.

We often use the following general symbol to show this.

^{17}O where the 17 represents the mass number or number of protons plus neutrons. Or in general

$$\mathop{}_{A}^{Z}O \quad \text{or} \quad \mathop{}_{A}^{Z}O^{c}$$

where A is the atomic number/ number of protons; Z is the mass number/ number of protons plus neutrons; and C is the net positive charge. Thus for our oxygen above if it were neutral A = 8; Z is 8 + 9 = 17 and have C = 8 since this is the number of positive protons and if it is neutral it is also the number of electrons.

For neutral uranium 238 the number of protons is 92 since uranium is element 92. The number of protons and neutrons is 238 and is Z. The number of neutrons is

$$Z = p + n$$

Then n = Z – p or 238 – 92 = 146. And, the number of electrons is 92 since the number of electrons is the same as the number of protons if it is neutral.

For sodium that has a net charge of + 1 with 12 neutrons we have the following. Z = 11 + 12 = 23; number of electrons is 11 – 1 = 10. A = 11.

CALCULATING ATOMIC MASS

The atomic mass is the number of protons plus the natural abundance of the various protons. Atoms with the same number of protons are the same element. Atoms with the same number of protons but different number of neutrons are called **isotopes**. Thus, hydrogen has three isotopes. The most abundant has one proton and no neutrons in the nucleus (over 99%). The next most abundant isotope has one proton and one neutron or two nucleons and is called deuterium. The third isotope has one proton and two neutrons and is called tritium. Most elements have isotopes. Tin has 10 isotopes.

The atomic mass or atomic weight is = fraction of isotope 1 times the mass of isotope one + fraction of isotope 2 times the mass of isotope two + etc. for each isotope.

For carbon the 12 isotope is present naturally in 98.9% of the carbon atoms with the other 1.1% having a mass number of 13. Thus the atomic weight is about $0.989 \times 12 + 0.011 \times 13 = 11.87 + 0.14 = 12.01$.

(Atomic mass unit = mass equal to one-twelfth the mass of a carbon which has a amu of 12.)

Question: What is the atomic weight of silicon, Si, that has three isotopes-28 that is present in a natural abundance of 92%, 29 present in 5% and 30 present in 3%.

Atomic weight = 28×0.92 (note not percentage but rather fraction) + $29 \times 0.05 + 30 \times 0.03 = 25.76 + 1.45 + 0.9 = 28.11$

PROBLEMS

1. What is the charge on an atom if it has lost one electron?

2. What product would you expect from the reaction on a boron cation with an oxygen anion?

3. Given ^{37}Cl how many protons, neutrons, and electrons (if it is neutral) are present? What is the mass number? What is the atomic number and atomic weight of chlorine?

4. How many protons, neutrons, and electrons (assuming the atom is neutral) does chlorine 35 have?

5. How many protons does cobalt have?

6. Name the subatomic particles, give their charge, and tell where they are located within an atom.

7. Name an alkaline earth

   Alkaline metal

   Halogen

   Rare or noble gas

8. Describe an element that has 38 electrons, and 36 protons. Which element is it? What is its net charge? What is its mass number?

9. Name two elements that have very similar properties to silicon.

10. Give the name of one halogen; one alkaline earth, one transition element and one rare or noble gas.

11. What is the atomic weight of an element that has 30% of the isotope 43 and the rest isotope 45?

12. Which of the following is a cation?

Na	Na^+
Al^{+3}	O_2

13. Which of the following is an anion?

Al	OH^-
O^{-2}	Br_2

13. Atoms are composed of mostly _____.

14. Oxygen atoms generally gain/lose ____ electrons when they react.

15. Sodium atoms generally gain/lose _____ electron(s) when they react.

16. The mass number for ^{41}Ca is _____.

17. In the periodic table, elements that typically lose electrons are found _____.

18. In the periodic table, elements that typically become anions when they react are found _____.

19. Using a period table, how many protons does barium element 56 have?

20. Using the periodic table how many electrons does a neutral titanium atom have?

21. Using the periodic table how many electrons does a chromium atom have if it has lost three electrons?

22. Using the designations metal, nonmetal, metalloid, which would you classify the following as

    Ti

    Cs

    P

23. Using the terms main group metal, main group nonmetal, and transition elements tell which the following would be described as.

    V

    Sr

    S

24. How are the elements arranged in the periodic table?

25. What are properties of an electron?

26. What are some properties of neutrons?

27. What element has 36 electrons when neutral?

28. What is the chemical symbol for silicon?

29. What is the chemical symbol for barium, boron, and bromine in that order?

30. What is the atomic weight of Ca?

31. Give the atomic number, atomic symbol, and atomic weight for potassium.

32. Which of the following is an alkaline metal?

    K, Sr, F, Ba, Li

33. Which of the following are alkaline earths?

    K, Sr, F, Ba, Li

34. Which of the following are(is) a halogen?

    K, Sr, F, Ba, Li

35. Name an element that is both a main group atom and a halogen.

36. Name an element that is both a transition metal and a metal.

37. Name an element that is both a main group element and a metal.

38. What is the charge of an iron atom that has lost two electrons?

39. What is an ion?

40. What is a cation?

ANSWERS

1. What is the charge on an atom if it has lost one electron?

   You can think of it in terms of a simple equation remembering that the charges on both sides of the equation must be the same and that an electron has a negative one charge.

$A \rightarrow A^+ + e^-$ so atom A has lost one electron and now has a positive one charge.

2. What product would you expect from the reaction on a boron cation with an oxygen anion?

   In the periodic table boron is in the 3A group of elements so it typically becomes a plus three by losing three electrons when it forms compounds and oxygen is in the 6A grouping of elements that normally gains two electrons becoming an oxygen minus two atom. For the compound to be neutral there would need to be two boron atoms, each with a net plus three giving a net plus 6 positive charge, and three oxygen ions, each with a negative two charge giving total 6 negative charge so the negative and positive charges would cancel. This can be looked at as follows.

   $$2\,B^{+3} + 3O^{-2} = B_2O_3$$

3. Given ^{37}Cl how many protons, neutrons, and electrons (if it is neutral) are present? What is the mass number? What is the atomic number and atomic weight of chlorine?

   First, since it is a chlorine element it has an atomic number of 17 which is the number of protons and also the number of electrons if the atom is neutral. (Note when an atom is neutral the number of protons is the same as the number of electrons. Why?) The superscript 37 is the mass number and is the total number of protons and neutrons. Thus, the number of neutrons is the mass number minus the number of protons.

   mass number = protons + neutrons

   neutrons = mass number − protons = 37 − 17 = 20 neutrons.

   We get the atomic weight from the periodic table unless additional information is given such as the number and amount of each isotope. From the periodic table the atomic weight is about 35.45 atomic mass units or 35.45 amu.

4. How many protons, neutrons, and electrons (assuming the atom is neutral) does chlorine 35 have?

   Again, because it is the element chlorine it has an atomic number of 17 which is the number of protons and if neutral the number of electrons. We get the number of protons as follows: neutrons = mass number − protons = 35 − 17 = 18 protons

5. How many protons does cobalt have?

   Cobalt has an atomic number of 27 so it has 27 protons.

6. Name the subatomic particles, give their charge, and tell where they are located within an atom.

   There are three subatomic particles.

   Proton- positive charge of one, found in the nucleus

   Neutron- no charge, found in the nucleus

   Electron- negative one charge, found around or about the nucleus or outside of the nucleus

7. Name an alkaline earth- beryllium, magnesium, calcium, strontium, barium, radium

   Alkaline metal -lithium, sodium, potassium, rubidium, cesium, or francium but **not** hydrogen

   Halogen - fluorine, chlorine, barium, iodine, astatine

   Rare or noble gas- helium, neon, argon, krypton, xenon, radon

8. Describe an element that has 38 electrons, and 36 protons. Which element is it?

   The element is krypton because it has 36 protons.

   What is its net charge? The addition of 38 minus and 36 positive give a net minus two

   What is its mass number? Cannot tell because the number of neutrons is not given.

9. Name two elements that have very similar properties to silicon.

   Any of the elements in the same family as silicon - carbon, germanium, tin, lead

10. Give the name of one halogen; one alkaline earth, one transition element and one rare or noble gas.

    Please look on the periodic table for this. Halogens-and element in Row7A; transition element- elements in the B rows; Rare/Nobel and elements in Row 8A.

11. What is the atomic weight of an element that has 30% of the isotope 43 and the rest isotope 45?

    The atomic mass or atomic weight is = fraction of isotope 1 times the mass of isotope one + fraction of isotope 2 times the mass of isotope two + etc. for each isotope.

    First, let us determine the percentage of isotope 45. Since there are only two isotopes and one is 30%, the remaining isotope is then $100 - 30 = 70\%$.

    Also, remember that we use the fraction and not percentage abundance for each isotope in our calculation. This is found by simply taking the percentage and dividing it by 100. So 70 % represents a fraction of 0.70 and 30% represents a fraction of 0.30.

    Atomic mass = $0.30 \times 43 + 0.70 \times 45 = 12.9 + 31.5 = 44.4$ amu

12. Which of the following is a cation?

    Na Na^+ cation

    Al^{+3} cation O_2

13. Which of the following is an anion?

    Al OH^- anion

    O^{-2} anion Br_2

14. Atoms are composed of mostly _____.

    Empty space.

15. Oxygen atoms generally gain/lose ____ electrons when they react.

    Gain; two

16. Sodium atoms generally gain/lose _____ electron(s) when they react.

Lose; one

17. The mass number for ^{41}Ca is _____.

41; already supplied in the question.

18. In the periodic table, elements that typically lose electrons are found _____.

to the left side such as Na, K, Ca

19. In the periodic table, elements that typically become anions when they react are found _____.

to the right such as O, F, Cl

20. Using a period table, how many protons does barium element 56 have?

56; simply the atomic number

21. Using the periodic table how many electrons does a neutral titanium atom have?

22; since it is neutral this is simply the atomic number

22. Using the periodic table how many electrons does a chromium atom have if it has lost three electrons?

$24 - 3 = 21$

23. Using the designations metal, nonmetal, metalloid, which would you classify the following as

Ti   metal
Cs   metal
P   nonmetal

24. Using the terms main group metal, main group nonmetal, and transition elements tell which the following would be described as.

V   transition metal
Sr   main group metal
S   main group nonmetal

25. How are the elements arranged in the periodic table?

Originally by property and weight but eventually by the number of protons and property with the number of protons being the deciding factor.

26. What are properties of an electron?

moves about the nucleus about 1/3 the speed of light, negatively changed, negative charge is equal in magnitude to the positive charge of the proton; relatively non-massive

27. What are some properties of neutrons?

found in the nucleus with protons; no charge-neutral; about the same mass as protons and more massive than electrons; becaues it is neutral it is the subatomic particle that is often used to bombard atoms since it is massive and not charged.

28. What element has 36 electrons when neutral?

Kr

29. What is the chemical symbol for silicon?

Si

30. What is the chemical symbol for barium, boron, and bromine in that order?

Ba, B, Br

31. What is the atomic weight of Ca?

40.08; from the periodic table

32. Give the atomic number, atomic symbol, and atomic weight for potassium.

19, K, 39.10

33. Which of the following is an alkaline metal?

K, Sr, F, Ba, Li

K and Li are alkaline metals

34. Which of the following are alkaline earths?

K, Sr, F, Ba, Li

Ba is the only alkaline earth of the group.

35. Which of the following are (is) a halogen?

K, Sr, F, Ba, Li

Only F is a halogen

36. Name an element that is both a main group atom and a halogen.

F, Cl, Br, I

37. Name an element that is both a transition metal and a metal.

any of the transition metals such as iron, gold, titanium

38. Name an element that is both a main group element and a metal.

Potassium, sodium, barium, aluminum

39. What is the charge of an iron atom that has lost two electrons?

+2; $Fe \rightarrow Fe^{+2} + 2e^-$

40. What is an ion?

An atom or group of atoms that have an excess or deficiency of electons compared with protons; that is, the number of protons does not equal to the number of electrons. They can be cations or anions.

41. What is a cation?

An atom or group of atoms that have a deficiency of electrons; that is, more protons than electrons. Examples are Ca^{+2} and NH_4^+

SAMPLE TEST PROBLEMS

Name _____ **Date** _____

Circle only correct answers.

42. Which is most massive? One atom of

a. Sr; b. Hf; c. Au; d. H; e. Cl.

43. Which atom has 22 protons in it?

a. Ru; b. Ti; c. Na; d. Ne; e. Hg.

44. What is the name of the family of compounds that has Ca, Mg, Ba, and Sr in it?

a. Rare gases; b. alkaline metals; c. inert materials; d. transition elements; e. alkaline earths.

45. Elements in the periodic table are arranged according to

a. number of electrons; b. number of protons; c. atomic weight;
d. electronegativities; e. number of subatomic particles.

46. Which of the following is the largest?

a. Rb; b. Mo; c. Co; d. Sb; e. S?

47. Which of the following is most simlilar in chemical properties to potassium?

a. calcium; b. sulfur; c. chlorine; d. sodium; e. cobalt.

48. Which compound would you believe was ionically bonded?

a. water; b. CO_2; c. LiBr; d. SiO_2; e. SO_2.

49. Which of the following is a metal?

a. Ti; b. K; c. Fe; d. Ca; e. all are metals.

50. Which of the following is a halogen?
a. chlorine; b. iron; c. tin; d. oxygen; e. carbon.

51. Which of the following is diatomic in nature?

a. bromine; b. hydrogen; c. oxygen; d. chlorine; e. all are diatomic.

52. Which chemical has the symbol Ca?

a. carbon; b. cobalt; c. chlorine; d. calcium; e. copper.

53. How many electrons does a neutral carbon atom have?

a. 6; b. 12; c. 3; d. 11; e. cannot tell.

54. If you add one electron and one neutron to a neutral atom of Cl what new element do you have?

a. argon; b. sulfur; c. fluorine; d. potassium; e. same element.

55. O^{-2} has _____ protons and _____ electrons.

a. 16, 18; b. 8, 10; c. 8, 6; d. 16, 8; e. 16, 14.

56. ^{14}C has _____ protons.

a. 6; b. 8; c. 10; d. 4; e. 14.

57. What is the atomic weight of an element that has two isotopes, 34% mass number of 65 and 66% mass number 35?

a. 45. 9;   b. 44.3;   c. 45.2;   d. 131;   e. 100.

58. What is the charge on a cobalt atom if 3 electrons are removed?

a. +1;   b. +2;   c. +3;   d. −3;   e. −2.

59. What is the mass number of an isotope with 123 protons and 120 neutrons?

a. 120;   b. 123;   c. 243;   d. 3;   e. cannot tell.

60. Complete the following: $Na \rightarrow Na^+ +$ _____

a. p^+,   b. calcium;   c. $2e^-$;   d. e^-;   e. n^o.

61. Which of the following is a main group element?

a. S;   b. C;   c. K;   d. Ca;   e. all are main group elements.

Molecules and Compounds

MOLECULES AND IONIC AND COVALENT COMPOUNDS

In general, molecules are formed from the combination of nonmetals. **Molecules** may be pure with only one kind of element such as diatomic oxygen, nitrogen, chlorine, and bromine. Or they can be compounds containing more than one kind of element. **Compounds** contain more than one kind of element. Compounds can be **ionic** derived from the combination of one or more metal ions and one or more nonmetal atoms or polyatomic ions. Compounds can also be **covalent** or molecules derived from more than one kind of nonmetal atom.

Examples of ionic compounds are sodium chloride, NaCl, and barium oxide, BaO. Examples of covalent compounds are nitrogen monooxide, NO, water, and common sugar. Compounds derived from polyvalent ions often contain both ionic and covalent bonding. Thus, $Ca(OH)_2$, calcium hydroxide, contains the Ca and two OH units that are attached to one another by ionic bonding but the polyvalent ion, the hydroxide ion, OH^{-1}, has the oxygen and hydrogen bonded together through covalent bonds.

REPRESENTATION OF COMPOUNDS

We use a short hand to represent compounds and elements. This short hand is also used to represent the elements in the Periodic Table. Thus, rather than hydrogen, we use the symbol or short hand H; and for oxygen we use O, etc.

For compounds we use a similar shorthand. Since common table salt contains one atom of sodium ion, Na^{+1}, for every atom of chloride ion, Cl^{-1}, we write the formula as NaCl.

For a simple sugar we have six carbons for every 12 hydrogen atoms and six oxygen atoms and we write this as $C_6H_{12}O_6$.

For the compound limestone, we have one calcium ion, Ca^{+2}, for every carbonate ion, CO_3^{-2}. Thus, limestone, or calcium carbonate, has a formula of $CaCO_3$. The carbonate radical has one carbon for every three oxygen atoms with a net minus two charge meaning that the carbonate radical has two more electrons than protons.

For sodium oxide we have **two** sodium ions, Na^{+1}, for every oxygen ion, O^{-2} because the overall net change for this compound is zero. The formula shorthand is then Na_2O.

Thus, **the suffixes tell the number of that particular atom it follows.**

Ionic compounds are formed where the tendency for one atom to want electrons compared with the other atom in the compound is so great that electrons are exchanged. Thus, the tendency for chlorine to want electrons compared with sodium that sodium given up and electron becoming Na^{+1} while chlorine takes on an electron becoming the chloride ion, $Cl^{-1.}$

$$Na \rightarrow Na^{+1} + e^- \text{ and}$$

$$Cl + e^- \rightarrow Cl^{-1}$$

Covalent compounds are formed when the tendency to attract electrons for the bonding atoms are similar. Thus, the tendency for sulfur and oxygen to attract electrons is similar resulting in the formation of a group of sulfur oxides many associated with acid rain. One of these sulfur oxides has one sulfur atom for every three oxygen atoms so its formula is SO_3.

NAMING OF SIMPLE COMPOUNDS- NOMENCLATURE

For our purposes of naming compounds we will consider metal-non-metal combinations as ionic compounds and combinations of non-metal atoms as covalent. Examples of ionic compounds are sodium chloride, NaCl, and calcium bromide, $CaBr_2$. Examples of covalent compounds are dinitrogen trioxide, N_2O_4, and phosphorus trifluoride, PF_3.

There are some so-called polyvalent anions and cations that you will also need to memorize. These are

Anions (negatively charged species)

Carbonate CO_3^{-2}	Phosphate PO_4^{-3}
Acetate $C_2H_3O_2^{-1}$	Nitrate NO_3^{-1}
Sulfate SO_4^{-2}	Hydroxide OH^{-1}

And

Cation (positively charged species)
Ammonium NH_4^{+1}

Naming- Divide into two groups.

Binary Inorganic Molecular/Covalent- composed of two non-metals

Binary Ionic-composed of a main group metal or metal with a variable oxidation number and non-metal and

the binary ionic is further subdivided into two groups as shown below.

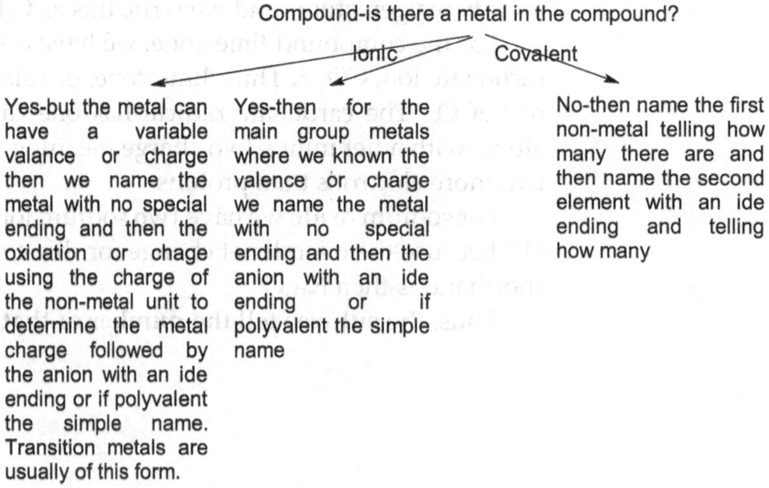

Compound-is there a metal in the compound?

Ionic   Covalent

Yes-but the metal can have a variable valance or charge then we name the metal with no special ending and then the oxidation or chage using the charge of the non-metal unit to determine the metal charge followed by the anion with an ide ending or if polyvalent the simple name. Transition metals are usually of this form.	Yes-then for the main group metals where we known the valence or charge we name the metal with no special ending and then the anion with an ide ending or if polyvalent the simple name	No-then name the first non-metal telling how many there are and then name the second element with an ide ending and telling how many

IONIC

Binary inorganic where we know the charge of valence of the metal- Thus, the IA elements all have a +1 charge (Na^{+1}, H^{+1}); 2A all have a +2 charge (Ba^{+2}, Ca^{+2}) and B and Al are generally +3 but Ga, In, and Tl can have a +3 or +5 so we need to check the anions to see which they are). Give name of metal-generally with an "ium" ending and then the name of the non-metal generally with an "ide" ending. For those derived from radicals, simply given the radical name

CaO	calcium oxide	$Ba(NO_3)_2$	barium nitrate
AlN	aluminum nitride	Na_3PO_4	sodium phosphate
NaCl	sodium chloride	LiBr	lithium bromide
KOH	potassium hydroxide	$CaCO_3$	calcium carbonate

Binary inorganic where the metal can have several different charges- The transition metals are generally of this variety as are some of the 4, 5, 6, etc. period elements of the main group. Thus, Group 4A metals Ge, Sn, and Pb can be a +2 or +4; Group 5A elements and metals such as P, As, Sb, and Bi and be +3 and +5. In these cases and in the case with transition metals we calculate the charge on the metal ion by observation of the charge given to the anions.

Steps. 1. Determine the anion charge.

2. Name the metal.

3. Give the metallic charge in Roman numerals as (charge) or simply give as charge without the (....) brackets

4. Give name of anion

CrO We know that oxygen forms an oxide with a −2 charge. Since the overall net charge of CrO is zero this means that Cr must be a +2 charge to balance the −2 charge. Thus, its name is chromium (II) oxide.

TiO_2 We know that each oxygen, oxide, is −2 and we have two of them for a net −4 charge. The charge on the Ti is then a +4 since the compound is neutral. The name is then titanium (IV) oxide.

$SnCl_4$ We know that each chlorine, now a chloride anion, is −1 and we have four of them so the net anion charge is $-1 \times 4 = -4$. Thus, the tin must be a +4 charge. The name is tin (IV) chloride.

$Co(OH)_3$ We know that each OH has a −1 charge. There are three OH units giving a total of −3. Thus, cobalt must be a +3. The name is cobalt (III) hydroxide.

Fe_2O_3 Each oxygen, now an oxide anion, has a charge of −2. We have three oxides so a total of $-2 \times 3 = -6$. This means that the cation must have a total charge of +6. But there are two irons so the charge of each iron is $+6/2 = 3$. (Note, the charge is for a **single** metal atom, here iron.) The name is iron (III) oxide.

COVALENT

Binary molecular (binary means two) For binary inorganic compounds of two non-metals need to give the number of atoms of each element along with the name of the first and then the number and name of the second element with an "ide" ending.

Number of atoms	Prefix	Number of atoms	Prefix
1	mono-	6	hexa-
2	di-	7	hepta-
3	tri-	8	octa-
4	tetra-	9	nona-
5	penta-	10	deca-

NO mononitrogen monooxide
or nitrogen monoxide
N_2O_4 dinitrogen tetraoxide

SO_2 sulfur dioxide
$ClBr_5$ chlorine pentabromide

FORMULAR (IONIC & COVALENT COMPOUNDS) AND MOLECULAR MASS (COVALENT COMPOUNDS)

**FORMULA MASS
OR FORMULA WEIGHT**

While there is a difference between formula mass and molecular mass often formula mass can be for **both** ionic and covalent compounds while molecular mass is restricted to covalent compounds. The terms mass and weight are different but we often use them interchangeably. We will do so here.

Formula mass is the sum of the atomic weights of all atoms in a compound or element. For sodium chloride, NaCl, this is 1 (number of sodium atoms in the formula) times 23 (mass of one mole of Na atoms) = 23 <u>PLUS</u> 1 (number of chloride atoms in the formula) times 35.5 (mass of one mole of chloride atoms) = 35.5 = 58.5 grams/mole.

This can be described as follows;
1 Na at 23 amu per Na = 23 amu
1 Cl at 35.5 amu per Cl = 35.5 amu
Total is then 23 + 35.5 = 58.5 amu

Or it can be described as
1 Na × 23 am/Na   = 23 amu
1 Cl × 35.5 amu/Cl = 35.5 amu
Total = 58.5 amu   = 58.5 grams/mole

We will find out that in every molar mass of a compound there is a mole and there is an Avogadro's number of that unit. For NaCl, every 58.5 grams of sodium chloride contains one mole of sodium chloride and one Avogadro's number of NaCl units or 6×10^{23} NaCl combinations or 6×10^{23} Na^{+1} and 6×10^{23} Cl^{-1} ions or a sum total of 2 times 6×10^{23} or 12×10^{23} total atoms.

For aluminum oxide, Al_2O_3 the formula weight is

2 Al × 27 amu/Al = 54 amu
3 O × 16 amu/O = 48 amu
Total   = 102 amu

Glass-largely SiO_2 (covalent   bonded) = 1×28 amu/silicon + 2×16 amu/oxygen = 60 amu or

1 Si × 28 amu/Si = 28 amu
2 O × 16 amu/O = 32 amu
Total   = 60 amu

NaOH (ionic bonded between the Na and OH units) 1×23 amu/sodium + 1×16 amu/oxygen + 1×1 amu/hydrogen = 40 amu or

1 Na × 23 amu/Na = 23 amu
1 O × 16 amu/O   = 16 amu
1 H × 1 amu/H   = 1 amu
Total   = 40 amu

Magnesium hydroxide-$Mg(OH)_2$ (ionic bonded between OH and Mg units)= 1×24.3 amu/magnesium $+2 \times 16$ amu/oxygen $+2 \times 1$ amu/hydrogen = 58.3 amu or

1 Mg $\times$ 24.3 amu/Mg = 24.3 amu
2 O $\times$ 16 amu/O   = 32 amu
2 H $\times$ 1 amu/H   = 2 amu
Total   = 58.3 amu

MOLECULAR WEIGHT OR MOLECULAR MASS

The **molecular weight** is the sum of the atomic weights of all atoms in a **covalently** bonded molecule of substance-compound or element.

The **molecular mass** for water is 2 hydrogen atoms times 1 amu for each hydrogen atoms plus 1 oxygen atom times 16 amu for each oxygen atom giving a total of 18 grams or grams/mole. Every 18 grams of water contains one mole of water molecules and one Avogadro's number of water molecules or 6×10^{23} water molecules. Again, we look at how many of each element are present. Since water has two hydrogen atoms and one oxygen atom there are $2 \times 6 \times 10^{23}$ hydrogen atoms and 6×10^{23} oxygen atoms. Or it can be calculated as follows:

1O $\times$ 16 amu/O = 16 amu
2H $\times$ 1 amu/H = 2 amu
Total = 18 amu = 18 grams/mole

Benzene-C_6H_6 (covalent bonded) = 6×12 amu/carbon $+6 \times 1$ amu/hydrogen = 78 amu ro

6 C $\times$ 12 amu/C = 72 amu
6 H $\times$ 1 amu/H = 6 amu
Total   = 78 amu

Acetone- CH_3COCH_3 (covalent bonded) = 3×12 amu/carbon $+6 \times 1$ amu/hydrogen $+1 \times 16$ amu/oxygen = 58 amu or

3 C $\times$ 12 amu/C = 36 amu
6 H $\times$ 1 amu/H = 6 amu
1 O $\times$ 16 amu/O = 16 amu
Total   = 58 amu

Dinitrogen tetraoxide-N_2O_4 (covalent bonded) = 2×14 amu/nitrogen $+4 \times 16$ amu/oxygen = 92 amu or
2 N $\times$ 14 amu/N = 28 amu
4 O $\times$ 16 amu/O = 64 amu
Total   = 92 amu

POLYATOMIC IONS AND ACID

Some atoms form groupings called polyatomic ions that often persist as reactions occur.

Know the following polyatomic ions

Cation-
  NH_4^+ Ammonium

Anions-
  CO_3^{-2} Carbonate

$C_2H_3O_2{}^-$	Acetate
$SO_4{}^{-2}$	Sulfate
$NO_3{}^-$	Nitrate
$PO_4{}^{-3}$	Phosphate
OH^-	Hydroxide

Acids-

Also know the following formats for naming acids.

Halides- Hydro--------ic Acid

HCl	Hydrochloric acid
HBr	Hydrobromic acid
HF	Hydrofluoric acid
HI	Hydroiodic acid

Misc. Acids

H_2SO_4	Sulfuric Acid
HNO_3	Nitric Acid
H_3PO_4	Phosphoric Acid
H_2CO_3	Carbonic Acid
$HC_2H_3O_2$	Acetic Acid

PROBLEMS

1. Name the following or give the formula of the following:
   Cobalt (II) nitrate
   Sodium nitride
   $FeSO_4$
   O_4S_6
   H_3PO_4

2. What is the name of the polyatomic anion in Na_3PO_4?

3. What is the formula mass of a molecule of $C_6H_4(OH)_2$?

4. In NO_2 how many oxygen molecules are there in it?

5. Name two elements that have very similar properties to titanium.

6. Give the formula or name for the following:
   Nickel (II) sulfate
   Platinum (IV) chloride
   Calcium oxide
   $CdSO_4$
   Se_2O

7. Name or give the formula for the following:
   Calcium chloride
   Dinitrogen tetraoxide
   Cobalt (III) chloride
   Cobalt (III) nitrate
   $NiCl_4$

8. Name or give the formula for the following:

S_4O_6

Sodium sulfate

Li_2CO_3

Aluminum phosphate

$Al(C_2H_3O_2)_3$

Barium hydroxide

9. Name the following as acids

HCl

H_3PO_4

10. Give the formula or name for the following:

NaCl

Iron (II) nitrate

Nitrogen dioxide

$C_3H_6O_3$

Water

Carbon dioxide

11. What is the chemical symbol for the following:

Arsenic

Bromine

Sodium

Boron

Iron

Phosphorus

12. What is the element including any charges for the following

A sodium atom that has lost one electron

An oxygen atom that has gained two electrons

Element 16 loses two protons and two electrons

Element 47 loses two neutrons and two electrons

13. What is the formula mass of a molecule of $C_6H_4(OH)_2$?

14. Which element is a halogen? I, C, Ti, Na

15. Which element is most similar in chemical properties to Na? Cl, C, Ca, K, U, Fe

16. Give the name/formula for the following:

Sulfur dichloride

Trioxygen difluoride

Chromium III sulfate

$Fe(NO_3)_2$

17. Name or give the formula for the following:

Na_3PO_4

NaH_2PO_4

HCl as a gas and acid

18. Name or give the formula for the following:

HNO_3

$NaHCO_3$

Phosphorus pentachloride

Dinitrogen tetrachloride

19. Name or give the formula for the following:

S_2O

CrO_3

$CoSO_4$

20. Name or give the formula for the following:

Nickel II nitrate dihydrate

Copper I chloride

Silver chloride

21. Name or give the formula for the following:

Silicon dioxide

Nitrogen trioxide

Water

Sodium hydroxide

22. Given that the cyanide anion is CN^{-1} what is the formula for mercury II cyanide?

23. Name or give the formula for the following:

H_2SO_4

Nitric acid

Barium hydroxide

24. Name or give the formula for the following:

Chromium IV nitrate

Nickel II nitrate

Gold I bromide

Vanadium II sulfate

25. Name or give the formula for the following:

Cr_2SO_4

Ammonium sulfate

Ammonium chloride

Ammonium nitrate

26. Name or give the formula for the following:

Disulfur hexafluoride

Arsenic pentabromide

Iron III phosphate

Lead II chloride/aka Lead dichloride

Tin tetrachloride/aka Tin IV chloride

27. What is the charge on an atom if it has gained one electron?

28. What product would you expect from the reaction of a calcium cation with a sulfur anion?

29. Given ^{120}Sn how many protons, neutrons, and electrons (if it is neutral) are present? What is the mass number? What is the atomic number and atomic weight of tin?

30. Name the following or give the formula of the following:

    Vanadium (II) nitrate

    Potassium sulfate

    $NiSO_4$

    S_4Cl_6

31. Name or give the formula for the following:

    HCl as an acid in water

    Cobalt (II) nitrate

    Lithium nitride

    $FeSO_4$

32. Name or give the formula for the following:

    O_2S_6

    H_3PO_4

    Titanium (II) sulfate

33. Name or give the formula for the following:

    Chromium (IV) chloride

    Calcium oxide

    $CaSO_4$

    S_2O

34. What is the name of the polyatomic anion in Li_3PO_4?

35. What is the formula mass of a molecule of $C_8H_3(OH)_3$?

36. What is the name of the polyatomic anion in K_2CO_3?

37. What is the name of the polyatomic ion is tripotassium phosphate?

38. What is the formula for iron II phosphate.

39. What is the name of the cation and anion in TiO_2.

40. Name two halogens.

41. If the boron cation were to react with the carbonate anion, what would you suspect would be its structural formula?

42. Which of the following are usually cations when present in ionic compounds? C, F, O, Ti, Sr.

43. Which of the following compounds are largely ionic? $CaCO_3$, iron II chloride; sodium bromide; sulfur dioxide

44. Which of the following has both ionic and covalent bonding? CaO; SrS; barium nitrate; titanium IV oxide.

45. For the space-filling models below, which model is most likely a model for antimony tribromide?

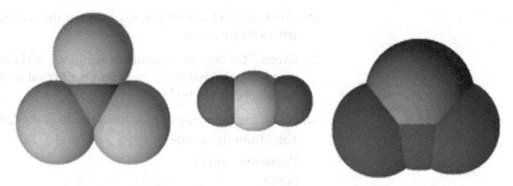

46. For the models shown for problem 45, which model is probably representing carbon dioxide?

47. For the three models shown in problem 45, which one is likely boron tribromide?

48. What is the oxidation number of all of the atoms in carbon dioxide?

49. What is the oxidation number for phosphorus in the phosphate radical?

50. What is the oxidation number of carbon is carbon tetrachloride.

51. What is the oxidation number for Cr in potassium dichromate, $K_2Cr_2O_7$?

52. What is the name of the following compounds.

53. What is the formula of the following compounds.

54. What is the charge for Cr in the compound CrO_2?

55. What is the name of the compound CrO_2?

56. Which of the following is considered an ionic compound? O_2, NaBr, $CaCO_3$, He, Kr

57. What is the name of the compound NH_4NO_3?

58. Name HF as an acid and as a gas that is not ionized.

59. What is the name of the compound that is formed from the combination of one iron ion with two oxygen atoms?

60. What is the weight of one mole of copper I carbonate?

61. Which of the following are molecules? CO_2, NH_3, H_2O, SO_2

62. One of the sugars has a formula $C_6H_{12}O_6$ for each molecule. How many different chemicals are in this sugar and how many total atoms are in one molecule of this sugar?

63. Which elements are diatomic?

SHORT EXAM

64. What is the charge on an atom if it has lost two electrons?
    a. 1; b. 2; c. −2; d. −1; e. zero

65. What product would you expect from the reaction on a aluminum cation with an oxygen anion?
    a. AlO; b. Al_2O; c. AlO_2; d. Al_2O_3; e. Al_3O_2

66–70. Name the following or give the formula of the following:

66. Cobalt (II) nitrate
a. $CoNO_3$; b. Co_2NO_3; c. $Co(NO_3)_2$; d. $Co(NO_2)_2$; e. None of the above

67. Sodium nitride:
a. $NaNO_3$; b. Na_3N; c. Na_2NO_3; d. Na_3NO_3; e. None of the above.

68. $FeSO_4$:
a. iron (II) nitrate; b. Iron (II) sulfate; c. Iron sulfate; d. iron sulfide; e. iron phosphate

69. O_4S_6:
a. oxygen sulfide; b. tetraoxide hexasulfide; c. tetraoxygen hexasulfide; d. oxygen hexasulfide; e. tetraoxide sulfur.

70. H_3PO_4:
a. trihydrogen phosphate; b. phosphorus acid; c. phosphoric acid; d. hydrogen phosphate; e. hydrogen phosphate.

71. What is the name of the polyatomic anion in Na_3PO_4?
a. sodium phosphate; b. carbonate; c. nitrate; d. sulfate; e. Phosphate.

72. What is the formula mass of a molecule of $C_6H_4(OH)_2$?
a. 110; b. 82; c. 65; d. 220; e. 154.

73. What is the formula weight of carbon tetrabromide?
a. 357; b. 168; c. 332; d. 86; e. 78.

74. What is the formula weight of oxygen hexabromide?
a. 368; b. 496; c. 827; d. 1624; e. 186.

75. What is the atomic weight of an element that has 60% of the isotope 53 and the rest isotope 45?
a. 44.4; b. 49.8; c. 48.6; d. 44.0; e. 44.8

76. Name an element that has very similar chemical properties to titanium.
a. Y; b. V; c. Zr; d. Fe; e. Co

77. Give the symbol of one halogen; one alkaline earth, one transition element in that order.
a. C, Pb, Co; b. Au, In, Sn; c. Ti, K, P; d. F, Ca, Ni; e. Ne; K, Be.

78. In SO_2 how many oxygen molecules are there in it?
a. 1; b. 2; c. 3; d. 4; e. 0

ANSWERS

1. Name the following or give the formula of the following:

Cobalt (II) nitrate	$Co(NO_3)_2$
Sodium nitride	Na_3N
$FeSO_4$	Iron II sulfate
O_4S_6	Tetraoxygen hexasulfide
H_3PO_4	Phosphoric Acid

2. What is the name of the polyatomic anion in Na_3PO_4?
Phosphate

3. What is the formula mass of a molecule of $C_6H_4(OH)_2$?

   $6C \times 12\ amu/C = 72\ amu$

   $6\ H \times 1\ amu/H = 6\ amu$

   $2O \times 16\ amu/O = 32\ amu$

   Total $= 110\ amu$

4. In NO_2 how many oxygen molecules are there in it?

   None. The oxygen is bonded to nitrogen and to one another or it would not be a compound.

5. Name two elements that have very similar properties to titanium.

   Zr and Hf

6. Give the formula or name for the following:

Nickel (II) sulfate	Ni_2SO_4
Platinum (IV) chloride	$PtCl_4$
Calcium oxide	CaO
$CdSO_4$	Cadmium II sulfate
Se_2O	Diselenium monooxide

7. Name or give the formula for the following:

Calcium chloride	$CaCl_2$
Dinitrogen tetraoxide	N_2O_4
Cobalt (III) chloride	$CoCl_3$
Cobalt (III) nitrate	$Co(NO_3)_3$
$NiCl_4$	Nickel IV chloride

8. Name or give the formula for the following:

S_2O_4	Disulfur tetraoxide
Sodium sulfate	Na_2SO_4
Li_2CO_3	Lithium carbonate
Aluminum phosphate	$AlPO_4$
$Al(C_2H_3O_2)_3$	Aluminum acetate
Barium hydroxide	$Ba(OH)_2$

9. Name the following as acids

HCl	Hydrochloric acid
H_3PO_4	Phosphoric acid

10. Give the formula or name for the following:

NaCl	Sodium chloride
Iron (II) nitrate	$Fe(NO_3)_2$
Nitrogen trioxide	NO_3
$C_3H_6O_3$	Have not had it
Water	H_2O
Carbon dioxide	CO_2

11. What is the chemical symbol for

Arsenic	As

Bromine	Br
Sodium	Na
Boron	B
Iron	Fe
Phosphorus	P

12. What is the element including any charges for the following

A sodium atom that has lost one electron

$$Na \rightarrow Na^+ + e^-$$

An oxygen atom that has gained two electrons

$$O + 2e^- \rightarrow O^{-2}$$

Element 16 loses two protons and two electrons

S in losing 2 protons is no longer sulfur but is Si. Since it lost 2 protons and 2 electrons there is no net charge.

Element 47 loses two neutrons and two electrons

Ag losing two neutrons does not change the element but the loss of two electrons means that it has a positive two change.

$$Ag \rightarrow Ag^{+2} + 2e^-$$

13. What is the formula mass of a molecule of $C_6H_4Cl_2$?

$6C \times 12$ amu/C	= 72 amu
$4H \times 1$ amu/H	= 4 amu
$2Cl \times 35.5$ amu/Cl	= 71 amu
Total	147 amu

14. Which element is a halogen? **I**, C, Ti, Na

15. Which element is most similar in chemical properties to Na? Cl, C, Ca, **K**, U, Fe

16. Give the name/formula for the following:

Sulfur dichloride	SCl_2
Trioxygen difluoride	O_3F_2
Chromium III sulfate	$Cr_2(SO_4)_3$
$Fe(NO_3)_2$	Iron II nitrate

17. Name or give the formula for the following:

Na_3PO_4	Sodium phosphate (sometimes this is referred to as trisodium phosphate)
NaH_2PO_4	Sodium dihydrogen phosphate
HCl as a gas and acid	Hydrogen chloride as a gas and hydrochloric acid as an acid

18. Name or give the formula for the following:

HNO_3	Nitric acid
$NaHCO_3$	Sodium hydrogen carbonate or sometimes by the common name sodium bicarbonate

Phosphorus pentachloride PCl_5
Dinitrogen tetrachloride N_2Cl_4

19. Name or give the formula for the following:

S_2O Disulfur monooxide
CrO_3 Chromium VI oxide
$CoSO_4$ Cobalt II sulfate

20. Name or give the formula for the following:

Nickel II nitrate dihydrate $Ni(NO_3)_2 \cdot 2H_2O$; hydrate is simply a name used to describe water thus a dihydrate means two water molecules for each nickel II nitrate unit

Copper I chloride $CuCl$ or sometimes you will see it as Cu_2Cl_2 as a dimer

Silver chloride $AgCl$ notice that though silver is a transition element since it is almost always a +1 charge in compounds the charge is generally omitted in naming compounds with silver in them.

21. Name or give the formula for the following:

Silicon dioxide SiO_2
Nitrogen trioxide NO_3
Water H_2O
Sodium hydroxide $NaOH$

22. Given that the cyanide anion is CN^{-1} what is the formula for mercury II cyanide?

Hg^{+2} requires 2 CN^- to give a neutral compound; $Hg(CN)_2$

23. Name or give the formula for the following:

H_2SO_4 Sulfuric acid
Nitric acid   Nitric acid
Barium hydroxide $Ba(OH)_2$

24. Name or give the formula for the following:

Chromium IV nitrate $Cr(NO_3)_4$
Nickel II nitrate $Ni(NO_3)_2$
Gold I bromide $AuBr$
Vanadium II sulfate VSO_4

25. Name or give the formula for the following:

Cr_2SO_4 Chromium I sulfate
Ammonium sulfate $(NH_4)_2SO_4$
Ammonium chloride NH_4Cl
Ammonium nitrate NH_4NO_3

26. Name or give the formula for the following:

Disulfur hexafluoride S_2F_6

Arsenic pentabromide	$AsBr_5$
Iron III phosphate	$FePO_4$
Lead II chloride/aka Lead dichloride	$PbCl_2$ (the aka is added simply to note that lead and tin and certain other metal and near-metal containing compounds can be named as either being metals or non-metals)
Tin tetrachloride/aka Tin IV chloride	$SnCl_4$

27. What is the charge on an atom if it has gained one electron?

$$A + e^- \rightarrow A^-$$

28. What product would you expect from the reaction on a calcium cation with a sulfur anion?

Calcium is a 2A element and loses two electrons when reacted giving a Ca^{+2} while sulfur takes on two electrons becoming S^{-2} so that a compound formed from the two to be electronically neutral will have one calcium and one sulfur, i.e. CaS.

29. Given ^{120}Sn how many protons, neutrons, and electrons (if it is neutral) are present? What is the mass number? What is the atomic number and atomic weight of tin?

Since tin is element 50, having an atomic number of 50, it has 50 protons and when neutral the same number of electrons, 50. The mass number is 120 and the number of protons is

neutrons = mass number − protons = 120 − 50 = 70 neutrons. The atomic weight, unless given more information, can be obtained from the periodic table and is 118.7.

30. Name the following or give the formula of the following:

Vanadium (II) nitrate	$V(NO_3)_2$
Potassium sulfate	K_2SO_4
$NiSO_4$	Nickel II sulfate
S_4Cl_6	Tetrasulfur hexachloride

31. Name or give the formula for the following:

HCl as an acid in water	Hydrochloric acid
Cobalt (II) nitrate	$Co(NO_3)_2$
Lithium nitride	Li_3N
$FeSO_4$	Iron II sulfate

32. Name or give the formula for the following:

O_2S_6	Dioxygen hexasulfide
H_3PO_4	Phosphoric acid
Titanium (II) sulfate	$TiSO_4$

33. Name or give the formula for the following:

Chromium (IV) chloride $\qquad$ $CrCl_4$

Calcium oxide $\qquad$ CaO

$CaSO_4$ $\qquad$ Calcium sulfate

S_2O $\qquad$ Disulfur monooxide

34. What is the name of the polyatomic anion in Li_3PO_4?
Phosphate

35. What is the formula mass of a molecule of $C_8H_3(OH)_3$?

$8C \times 12\,amu/C = 96\,amu$

$6H \times 1\,amu/H = 6\,amu$

$3O \times 16\,amu/O = 48\,amu$

Total $\qquad = 150\,amu$

36. What is the name of the polyatomic anion in K_2CO_3 ?
Carbonate

37. What is the name of the polyatomic ion is tripotassium phosphate?
Phosphate.

38. What is the formula for iron II phosphate.
$Fe_3(PO_4)_2$

39. What is the name of the cation and anion in TiO_2.
Cation is titanium and anion is oxygen or oxide.

40. Name two halogens.
Chlorine, bromine, iodine, fluorine.

41. If the boron cation were to react with the carbonate anion, what would you suspect would be its structural formula?

B reacts as it is B^{+3} and the carbonate anion is CO_3^{-2} so to give a neutral compound it will be $B_2(CO_3)_3$.

42. Which of the following are usually cations when present in ionic compounds? C, F, O, Ti, Sr.

Sr and Ti are metals and typically form positively changed cations in compounds.

43. Which of the following compounds are largely ionic? $CaCO_3$, iron II chloride; sodium bromide; sulfur dioxide

Only sulfur dioxide is not an ionic compound.

44. Which of the following has both ionic and covalent bonding? CaO; SrS; barium nitrate; titanium IV oxide.
Only barium nitrate contains both ionic, connecting the barium to the nitrate radical, and covalent bonding present in the carbonate radical.

45. For the space-filling models below, which model is most likely a model for antimony tribromide?

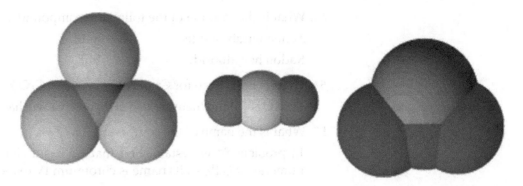

Antimony tribromide will take a tetrahedral structure with one unbonded electron pair not shown. Thus, $SbBr_3$ is probably the model on the right side.

46. For the models shown for problem 45, which model is probably representing carbon dioxide?

CO_2 is linear with carbon in the middle and the oxygen atoms on either side. The model in the center is most likely carbon dioxide.

47. For the three models shown in problem 45, which one is likely boron tribromide?

Boron tribromide, BBr_3 is trigonal planar and is probably the structure shown to the left.

48. What is the oxidation number of all of the atoms in carbon dioxide?
Oxygen is -2 so it is the carbon atoms that are in question. There are 2 oxygen atoms giving a net -4 so carbon, in order to form a neutral compound is $+4$.

49. What is the oxidation number for phosphorus in the phosphate radical?
The phosphate radical is PO_4^{-3} so that unlike many of our other examples where the sum total of the oxidation numbers is zero, that is the compound is neutral, the phosphate radical is a net -3. each O is a -2 and we have four of them for a total of -8. We ask the question, what do we add to a -8 so that the net is a -3, the charge of the entire phosphate radical. The answer is $+5$. So, phosphorus is then a $+5$.

50. What is the oxidation number of carbon is carbon tetrachloride.

Each Cl is a minus one giving a total for the four Cls of -4. Carbon is then $+4$ so that the compound is neutral as given.

51. What is the oxidation number for Cr in potassium dichromate, $K_2Cr_2O_7$?

Each potassium is a $+1$ for a total of $+2$ since there are two potassium ions in the structure. Each O is -2×7 oxygen atoms gives a total of -14. We have only chromium remaining. We ask the question what do we add to a -14 and $+2$ to get zero, since this compound is neutral. The answer is $+12$. But, we remember that oxidation numbers are for single atoms and we have two chromium atoms. Thus, the oxidation number for a single chromium atom is $+12/2$ the number of chromium atoms) $= +6$. thus the oxidation number for chromium is $+6$.

52. What is the name of the following compounds.

$SbCl_3$	Antimony trichloride or antimony III chloride
$SbCl_5$	Antimony pentachloride or antimony V chloride

53. What is the formula of the following compounds.

Xenon tetrabromide $XeBr_4$

Radon hexafluoride RnF_6

54. What is the charge for Cr in the compound CrO_2?

Each O is −2 and there are two of them so Cr will have a charge of IV or +4.

55. What is the name of the compound CrO_2?

In problem 54 we established that Cr has a charge of +4, in Roman numerals it is IV, so its name is chromium IV oxide.

56. Which of the following is considered an ionic compound? O_2, NaBr, $CaCO_3$, He, Kr

The ionic compounds are NaBr and $CaCO_3$. In fact the other three of the possibilities are not even compounds but rather elements.

57. What is the name of the compound NH_4NO_3?

This compound is composed of two polyatomic ions and takes on the name of both of the polyatomic ions-ammonium and nitrate becoming ammonium nitrate.

58. Name HF as an acid and as a gas that is not ionized.

As an acid it is hydrofluoric acid and as a gas that is not ionized it is named hydrogen fluoride. In point of fact HF is a weak acid.

59. What is the name of the compound that is formed from the combination of one iron ion with two oxygen atoms?

The compound is FeO_2 and is named iron IV oxide.

60. What is the weight of one mole of copper I carbonate?

The carbonate radical has a net charge of −2 so we will need two copper +1 atoms to balance this −2. Thus, the formula is Cu_2CO_3. Because copper is almost always a +1 charge sometimes we will see this compound simply named copper carbonate.

2Cu × 63.5 amu/Cu = 127 amu

1C × 12 amu/C   = 12 amu

3O × 16 amu/O   = 48 amu

Total   = 187 amu = 187 g/mole.

61. Which of the following are molecules? CO_2, NH_3, H_2O, SO_2

All are molecules and all are covalently bonded.

62. One of the sugars has a formula $C_6H_{12}O_6$ for each molecule. How many different chemicals are in this sugar and how many total atoms are in one molecule of this sugar?

There are three different chemicals-C, H, O. The total number of atoms is simply 6 C + 12 H + 6 O = 24 total atoms.

63. Which elements are diatomic?

H_2, N_2, O_2, and F_2, Cl_2, Br_2, I_2 that is all of the halogens.

SAMPLE TEST PROBLEMS

Name _____ Date _____

Circle only correct answers.

64. What is the charge on an atom if it has lost two electrons?
a. 1; b. 2; c. −2; d. −1; e. zero

65 What product would you expect from the reaction on a aluminum cation with an oxygen anion?
a. AlO; b. Al_2O; c. AlO_2; d. Al_2O_3; e. Al_3O_2

66–70. Name the following or give the formula of the following:

66. Cobalt (II) nitrate
a. $CoNO_3$; b. Co_2NO_3; c. $Co(NO_3)_2$; d. $Co (NO_2)_2$; e. None of the above

67. Sodium nitride:
a. $NaNO_3$; b. Na_3N; c. $Na_2 NO_3$; d. $Na_3 NO_3$; e. None of the above.

68. $FeSO_4$:
a. iron (II) nitrate; b. Iron (II) sulfate; c. Iron sulfate; d. iron sulfide; e. iron phosphate

69. O_4S_6:
a. oxygen sulfide; b. tetraoxide hexasulfide; c. tetraoxygen hexasulfide; d. oxygen hexasulfide; e. tetraoxide sulfur.

70. H_3PO_4:
a. trihydrogen phosphate; b. phosphorus acid; c. phosphoric acid; d. hydrogen phosphate; e. hydrogen phosphate.

71. What is the name of the polyatomic anion in Na_3PO_4?
a. sodium phosphate; b. carbonate; c. nitrate; d. sulfate; e. Phosphate.

72. What is the formula mass of a molecule of $C_6H_4(OH)_2$?
a. 110; b. 82; c. 65; d. 220; e. 154.

73. What is the formula weight of carbon tetrabromide?
a. 357; b. 168; c. 332; d. 86; e. 78.

74. What is the formula weight of oxygen hexabromide?
a. 368; b. 496; c. 827; d. 1624; e. 186.

75. What is the atomic weight of an element that has 60% of the isotope 53 and the rest isotope 45?
a. 44.4; b. 49.8; c. 48.6; d. 44.0; e. 44.8

76. Name an element that has very similar chemical properties to titanium.
a. Y; b. V; c. Zr; d. Fe; e. Co

77. Give the symbol of one halogen; one alkaline earth, one transition element in that order.
a. C, Pb, Co; b. Au, In, Sn; c. Ti, K, P; d. F, Ca, Ni; e. Ne; K, Be.

78. In SO_2 how many oxygen molecules are there in it?
a. 1; b. 2; c. 3; d. 4; e. 0

Chemical Composition

MOLE AND AVOGARDO'S NUMBER

Mole- is not a furry creature that digs in our yards but it is a counting unit. Formally, a MOLE-is the amount of a substance that contains as many elementary entities (atoms, molecule, etc.) as there are atoms in exactly 12 g of the carbon-12 isotope.

One mole contains 6×10^{23} units. This number is called **Avogadro's Number**. The **Atomic Mass Number** of an element, or SUMMATION of Atomic mass numbers in a compound will have Avogadro's Number of atoms (for mono-atomic elements) or formula units (compounds) in it.

The **Molar Mass** of an element or compound is numerically equal to the atomic mass in atomic mass units-which for us is simply the atomic weights or atomic masses we find for the individual elements from the periodic table.

Thus, as you look at the periodic table, the atomic weight for each element is the weight in grams that contains one mole or one Avogadro's number of that element's atoms. Thus, the atomic weight of titanium is about 48; so in every 48 grams of titanium there is one mole of titanium and there is one Avogadro's number of titanium; there are 6×10^{23} titanium atoms.

The appropriate or right unit for molar mass is grams per mole or g/mol.

The molar mass of Al = 27. Thus there are Avogadro's Number of aluminum atoms in 27 grams of aluminum. Or the molar mass for Al is 27 grams/mole.

The molar mass of water, H_2O, is 2 (number of hydrogens) times 1 (mass of one mole of hydrogen atoms) = 2 PLUS 1 (number of oxygen atoms) times 16 (mass of one mole of oxygen atoms) = 18 grams/mole.

DETERMINATION OF NUMBER OF MOLES FROM WEIGHT

An important formula for you to memorize and have a good working knowledge of is

$$\text{Number moles} = \frac{\text{Weight}}{\text{GFW}}$$

for both ionic and covalently bonded compounds and

$$\text{Number of moles} = \frac{\text{Weight}}{\text{GMW}}$$

for covalently bonded materials.

Please remember that the "weights" we use are generally in grams unless directed to do otherwise.

Following are problems that illustrate the use of molar mass and how to calculate the number of moles from a given weight.

Number of moles in 180 grams of NaCl is 180 grams/58.5 grams/mole = 3.07 moles.

Number of moles of water in 0.50 grams of water is 0.50 grams/ 18 grams/mole = 0.028 moles.

Number of moles of water in 30 ml of water. Assume density of water is 1 gram/ml. $D = M/V$ & $M = D \times V = 1 \text{ g/ml} \times 30 \text{ ml} = 30$ grams. # Moles = 30 grams/18 grams/mole = 1.7 moles.

DETERMINATION OF WEIGHT FROM NUMBER OF MOLES AND FORMULA WEIGHT

Another important equation for you to know and have a good working knowledge of related the number of molecules or gram formula units is actually derived from the relationship used to calculate number of moles.

Number of moles = weight in grams/gram formula weight = wt/gfw

$$\text{Number moles} = \frac{\text{Weight}}{\text{GFW}}$$

If we cross multiply we get our new equation that relates number weight to the number of moles as

Weight = number of moles × gram formula weight

DETERMINATION OF NUMBER OF UNITS FROM NUMBER OF MOLES AND AVOGADRO'S NUMBER

We have an additional important equation that we need to know and know how to use. It relates the number of moles to the number of units.

Number of units = number of moles × Avogadro's Number
Remember that
One mole = one formula (or molecular weight) and that
One gram mole = one formula (or molecular weight) in grams and that
One gram mole has within it one Avogadro's Number of units.
More mole-related problems follow.

Q. How many grams of water are in ½ moles of water.

A. We have that number moles = Wt /GFW. We can rearrange this to solve for Wt = # moles times GFW. Thus, Weight = ½ mole times 18 grams/mole = 9 grams.

Q. How many molecules of water are in 9 grams of water?

A. Remember that one gram mole, one gram formula weight and one gram molecular weight have 6×10^{23} units or molecules

Thus, # of molecules = # moles $\times$ 6×10^{23} molecules/mole =

0.5 moles $\times$ 6×10^{23} molecules/mole = 3×10^{23} molecules

Q. What is the weight of one molecule of water.

A. We know that 6×10^{23} molecules weigh 18 grams or that there are 6×10^{23} molecules/gram formula (molecular) weight and for water there is 18 grams/gram formula (molecular) weight-thus

$$\frac{18 \text{ grams/gram molecular weight}}{6 \times 10^{23} \text{ molecules/gram molecular weight}} = 3 \times 10^{-23} \text{ grams}$$

We can also set this up as a simple proportion as follows. We remember that one mole weights one GFW and has 6×10^{23} units so

$$\frac{18 \text{ grams}}{\text{X grams}} = \frac{6 \times 10^{23} \text{ water molecules}}{1 \text{ water molecule}}$$

Cross multiplication and solving for $\times$ the weight of one water molecule gives

X grams = 18 grams $\times$ 1 water molecule/6 $\times$ 10^{23} water molecules = 3 $\times$ 10^{-23} grams

Q. Given 160 grams of sodium hydroxide, NaOH, how many moles, repeat units and sodium atoms are there.

A. First, determine the gram formula weight of NaOH.

1 $\times$ 23 amu/Sodium + 1 $\times$ 1 amu/hydrogen + 1 $\times$ 16 amu/oxygen = 40 amu or 40 grams/mole or 40 grams/6 $\times$ 10^{23} units of NaOH
The number of moles is
Number moles = mass/gram formula weight = 160 grams/40 grams/mole = 4 moles

Number repeat units = 4 moles $\times$ 6 $\times$ 10^{23} repeat units/mole = 24 $\times$ 10^{23} repeat units = 2.4 $\times$ 10^{24} repeat units in scientific notation to two significant figures.

Number of sodium atoms is equal to the number of NaOH units since each gram formula weight of NaOH has one sodium aotm.

MASS PERCENTAGE COMPOSITIONS

Mass percentage compositions are determined from the formula

$$\% \text{ Mass Composition} = \frac{\text{Mass of element}}{\text{Total mass}} \times 100$$

Q. What is the % of H, O and Na in NaOH (by mass, not number)?

A. Determine the formula weight.
1 $\times$ 1 amu/hydrogen = 1 amu
1 $\times$ 16 amu/oxygen = 16 amu
1 $\times$ 23 amu/sodium = 23 amu
Total = 40 amu or 40 g/mole

$$\% \text{ H} = (1/40) \times 100 = 2.5 \% \text{ hydrogen}$$

$$\% \text{ O} = (16/40) \times 100 = 40 \% \text{ oxygen}$$

$$\% \text{Na} = (23/40) \times 100 = 57.5 \% \text{ sodium}$$

Sum total of 2.5 + 40 + 57.5 = 100 %

Q. What is the % carbon and hydrogen in benzene, C_6H_6?

A. Determine the molecular weight of benzene.

$$6 \times 12 \text{ amu/carbon} = 72 \text{ amu}$$

$$6 \times 1 \text{ amu/hydrogen} = 6 \text{ amu}$$

$$\text{Total} = 78 \text{ amu or } 78 \text{ g/mole}$$

Now we will calculate the percentage of each element from the contribution each elements made to the total formula weight.

$$\% \text{ C} = (72/78) \times 100 = 92 \%$$

$$\% \text{ H} = (6/78) \times 100 = 8 \%$$

Sum total is 100 %.

EMPIRICAL FORMULAS FOR COMPOUNDS

Typically, for this kind of problem the percentage of each element is given. Each percentage is divided by a "leveling" factor, the atomic weight for that element. This gives a value that is then divided by the lowest or least value giving the number of each element in the empirical formula. A strategy sequence might be

% Element → divide % element by atomic weight for that element → divide by smallest values → empirical formula

Problem: What is the empirical formula for a compound that has 27.3 % carbon and 72.7 % oxygen by weight. We believe the compound has only carbon and oxygen since the two percentages add to 100%.

$$\text{C fraction} = \frac{27.3}{12 \text{ (atomic weight of carbon)}} = 2.3$$

$$\text{O fraction} = \frac{72.7}{16} = 4.5$$

This means that for every 2.3 carbon atoms there are 4.5 carbon atoms. We will now divide each of these values by the smallest value, 2.3.

For carbon we get 2.3/2.3 = 1
and for oxygen we get 4.5/2.3 = 2.

Thus there are in the compound one carbon and two oxygen atoms giving an empirical formula of CO_2.

Problem: What is the empirical formula for a compound that has 57.5 % sodium, 2.5 % hydrogen, and 40 % oxygen.

As above, we will divide each percentage by the atomic weight of the particular element.

$$\text{Na } 57.5/23 = 2.5$$

$$\text{H } 2.5/1 = 2.5$$

$$\text{O } 40/16 = 2.5$$

We now divide each value by the smallest which in all cases is 2.5. Thus, each of these values are one so the empirical formula has one sodium, one oxygen, and one hydrogen in it. The empirical formula is NaOH.

MOLECULAR FORMULAS FROM PERCENTAGE COMPOSITION

Here, we determine the empirical formula and from the given molecular weight calculate the number of repeat empirical formulas are in compound and then multiple the empirical formula by that number.

Empirical formula → Molecular Formula

Problem: What is the molecular formula for a compound with 7.69 % hydrogen and 92.3 % carbon and a molecular weight of 78.

Empirical Formula

$$\text{H } 7.69/1 = 7.69$$

$$\text{C } 92.3/12 = 7.69$$

Division of each by the smallest number, which is the same giving one hydrogen to every one carbon for an empirical formula of CH.

The formula weight for the empirical formula is

$$1\,C \times 12\,amu/C = 12\,amu$$

$$1\,H \times 1\,amu/H = 1\,amu$$

$$Total = 13\,amu/unit.$$

The number of empirical formulas is the molecular weight/ formula weight for the empirical formula and for here 78/13 = 6. Thus, there are 6 empirical units or 6(CH) = C_6H_6 for the molecular formula.

It is important to remember that the molecular formula can vary from the empirical formula for covalent compounds that actually form molecules. By comparison, the empirical formula for ionic compound is generally the same as the formula for the compound since for ionic compounds the formulas are generally simply the simplest ratio of elements that compose it. Thus, for NaCl the empirical and the formula for the compound are the same since the formula simply represents that in sodium chloride there is a one to one ratio of Na and Cl.

PROBLEMS

1. Given that phenol has 76.6% carbon, 6.38% hydrogen and 17.0% oxygen, what is its empirical formula?

2. Given that benzene is 92.3 % carbon and 7.69 % hydrogen what is its empirical formula? What is its molecular formula if its molecular weight is 78 amu?

3. Diethylether is the "ether" in the old movies that was used to put people asleep. It has 64.9 % carbon, 13.5 % hydrogen, and 21.6 % oxygen. What is its empirical formula?

4. What is the percentage of sodium, sulfur, and oxygen in sodium sulfate?

5. What is the percentage chromium, nitrogen, and oxygen in chromium (III) nitrate?

6. What is the empirical formula for a compound containing carbon = 62.07%; hydrogen = 10.34 % and oxygen = 27.59%? What is its molecular formula if its molecular weight is 58 amu?

7. What is the empirical formula for a compound containing 29.4% calcium; 23.5% sulfur; and 47.1% oxygen? And what is its name?

8. What is the empirical formula for a compound that contains sodium, hydrogen and oxygen if it contains 57.5% sodium and 2.5% hydrogen? And what is its name?

9. What is the formula weight of carbon tetrachloride?

10. What is the formula weight of sulfur hexabromide?

11. How many moles of oxygen dibromide are there in 56 grams? How many molecules are there in the 56 grams?

12. How many moles of iron (III) phosphate are there in 186 grams?

13. A somewhat strange and toxic compound was found in a cave. It has the following composition: % Fe = 41.8; % C = 26.9; % N = 31.3. What is its empirical formula?

14. Another compound was found in the same cave with the main element having two isotopes- 51% isotope 178 and the remainder isotope 179. What is its atomic mass? Which of the following elements is it most likely to be Y, Hf, C, Pt?

15. If you remove 2 electrons and 3 neutrons from Ag, what element would it be?

16. What is the percentage weight of oxygen in iron II sulfate?

17. How many moles of titanium IV nitrate are in 150 grams?

18. What is the mass of one molecule of carbon tetrachloride?

19. What is the formula mass of mercury II nitrate?

20. Name the following compounds:
$Zn(NO_3)_2$
$Fe_2(SO_4)_3$
S_2Br_6
$Ca_3(PO_4)_2$

21. Polytetrafluoroethylene (Teflon) is made from the monomer tetrafluoroethylene which has 24% carbon and 76% fluorine. What is its empirical formula?

22. How many moles are in 36 grams of water?

23. How many molecules are in 36 grams of water?

24. How many atoms are in 36 grams of water?

25. How many grams are in 0.4 moles of sodium hydroxide?

26. In SO_2 how many oxygen molecules are there in it?

27. What is the atomic weight of an element that has 70% of the isotope 43 and 30% isotope 45?

28. What is the weight of one atom of carbon dioxide?

29. How many moles calcium nitrate are in 60 grams of calcium nitrate?

30. What is the answer to problem 29 to two significant figures in scientific notation?

ANSWERS

1. Given that phenol has 76.6% carbon, 6.38% hydrogen and 17.0% oxygen, what is its empirical formula?

Elem	%	%/At Wt	Div by Smallest Number
C	76.6	76.6/12 = 6.35	6.35/1.06 = 5.99 or about 6
H	6.38	6.38/1 =6.38	6.38/1.06 = 6.02 or about 6
O	17.0	17.0/16 = 1.06	1.06/1.06 = 1

Thus empirical formula has 6 carbon atoms, 6 hydrogen atoms, and one oxygen atom giving an empirical formula of C_6H_6O.

2. Given that benzene is 92.3 % carbon and 7.69 % hydrogen what is its empirical formula? What is its molecular formula if its molecular weight is 78 amu?

Elem	%	%/AtWt	Div by Smallest Number
C	92.3	92.3/12 = 7.69	7.69/7.99 = 1
H	7.69	7.69/1= 7.69	7.69/7.99 = 1

Thus the empirical formula has one carbon and one hydrogen, CH.

The molecular formula is best determined by looking at the mass of the empirical formula, in this case

$$1C \times 12 \, amu/C = 12$$

$$1H \times 1 \, amu/H = 1$$

Total = 13 amu for the empirical formula. The next step is to see how many empirical formula units are in the molecular formula. To do this we simply divide the molecular weight by the mass for the empirical formula; 78/13 = 6 so that there are 6 empirical units in the molecular formula or 6(CH) = C_6H_6 as the molecular formula.

We can check this by simply computing the molecular weight for the proposed molecular formula and it should be the same as the supplied molecular weight.

$$6C \times 12 \, amu/C = 72$$

$$6H \times 1 \, amu/H = 6$$

$$Total = 78 \, amu.$$

3. Diethylether is the "ether" in the old movies that was used to put people asleep. It has 64.9 % carbon, 13.5 % hydrogen, and 21.6 % oxygen. What is its empirical formula?

Elem	%	%/AtWt	Div by Smallest Number
C	64.9%	64.9/12 = 5.41	5.41/1.35 = 4.00
H	13.5%	13.5/1 = 13.5	13.5/1.35 = 10.0
O	21.6%	21.6/16 = 1.35	1.35/1.35 = 1.00

Thus, the empirical formula has 4 carbon atoms, 10 hydrogen atoms and 1 oxygen atom and is expressed at $C_4H_{10}O$

4. What is the percentage of sodium, sulfur, and oxygen in sodium sulfate?

The first step is to correctly give the formula for sodium sulfate. Sodium sulfate's formula is Na_2SO_4.

Next, need to get the formula weight for sodium sulfate.

$$2Na \times 23 \, amu/Na = 46 \, amu$$

$$1S \times 32 \, amu/S = 32 \, amu$$

$$4 \, O \times 16 \, amu/O = 64 \, amu$$

$$Total = 142 \, amu$$

Next we calculate the percentage of each element by dividing the contribution for that particular element by the total weight, formula weight, and multiple by 100 to convert the answer to percentage.

$$\% \text{ Na} = (46/142) \times 100 = 32.4$$

$$\%\text{S} = (32/142) \times 100 = 22.5$$

$$\%\text{O} = (64/142) \times 100 = 45.1$$

$$\text{Total} = 100\%$$

5. What is the percentage chromium, nitrogen, and oxygen in chromium (III) nitrate?

We first determine the correct formula for chromium III nitrate to be $Cr(NO_3)_3$.

The formula weight is then calculated.

$$1\text{Cr} \times 52 \text{ amu/Cr} = 52 \text{ amu}$$

$$3\text{N} \times 14 \text{ amu/N} = 42 \text{ amu}$$

$$9\text{O} \times 16 \text{ amu/O} = 144 \text{ amu}$$

$$\text{Total} = 238 \text{ amu}$$

Next we calculate the percentage of each element by dividing the contribution for that particular element by the total weight, formula weight, and multiple by 100 to convert the answer to percentage.

$$\% \text{ Cr} = (52/238) \times 100 = 21.8$$

$$\% \text{ N} = (42/238) \times 100 = 17.6$$

$$\% \text{ O} = (144/238) \times 100 = 60.5$$

$$\text{Total} = 99.9$$

The total of the percentages should be 100 but because of "rounding errors" where numbers are rounded off, the percentage may be a little over or under 100 as in this case.

6. What is the empirical formula for a compound containing carbon = 62.07%; hydrogen = 10.34 % and oxygen = 27.59%? What is its molecular formula if its molecular weight is 58 amu?

Elem	%	%/AtWt	Div by Smallest Number
C	62.07	62.07/12 = 5.173	5.173/1.724 = 3.00
H	10.34	10.34/1 = 10.34	10.34/1.724 = 6.00
O	27.59	27.59/16 = 1.724	1.724/1.724 = 1.00

Thus, the empirical formula is C_3H_6O

The empirical formula weight is

$$3\,\text{C} \times 12\text{amu/C} = 36 \text{ amu}$$

$$6\,\text{H} \times 1 \text{ amu/H} = 6 \text{ amu}$$

$$1\,\text{O} \times 16 \text{ amu/O} = 16 \text{ amu}$$

Total = 58 amu for one units. Since the molecular weight is 58 amu then the empirical formula and molecular formula are the same.

7. What is the empirical formula for a compound containing 29.4% calcium; 23.5% sulfur; and 47.1% oxygen? And what is its name?

Elem	%	%/AtWt	Div by Smallest Number
Ca	29.4	29.4/40 = 0.735	0.735/0.734 = 1
S	23.5	23.5/32 = 0.734	0.734/0.734 = 1
O	47.1	47.1/16 = 2.94	2.94/0.734 = 4

Empirical formula is $CaSO_4$ which is the formula for calcium sulfate.

8. What is the empirical formula for a compound that contains sodium, hydrogen and oxygen if it contains 57.5% sodium and 2.5% hydrogen? What is its name?

First, knowing that the total is 100 %, we can calculate the % O as follows.

100- 57.5 - 2.5 = 40.0 % which is the percentage O.

Elem	%	%/AtWt	Div by Smallest Number
Na	57.5	57.5/23 = 2.5	2.5/2.5 = 1
O	40.0	40.0/16 = 2.5	2.5/2.5 = 1
H	2.5	2.5/1 = 2.5	2.5/2.5 = 1

So the empirical formula is the formula NaOH and its name is sodium hydroxide.

9. What is the formula weight of carbon tetrachloride?

For these problems the first step is to get the formula correct from the name.

Carbon tetrachloride is CCl_4.

$$1C \times 12 \text{ amu/C} = 12 \text{ amu}$$

$$4Cl \times 35.5 \text{ amu/Cl} = 142 \text{ amu}$$

Formula weight is then   154 amu.

10. What is the formula weight of sulfur hexabromide?

Sulfur hexabromide is SBr_6

$$1S \times 32 \text{ amu/S} = 32 \text{ amu}$$

$$6Br \times 80 \text{ amu/Br} = 480 \text{ amu}$$

Formula weight is   512 amu

11. How many moles of oxygen dibromide are there in 56 grams? How many molecules are there in the 56 grams?

First, we need to deduce the correct formula from the name oxygen dibromide. The formula is OBr_2.

Next we will get the formula weight since the number of moles is

Weight/formula weight = moles

$$1O \times 16 \text{ amu/O} = 16 \text{ amu}$$

$$2Br \times 80 \text{ amu/Br} = 160 \text{ amu}$$

Formula weight = 176 amu

moles = weight/formula weight = 56 g/176 g/mole = 0.32 moles. Notice that we used the unit g/mole for the formula weight.

12. How many moles of iron (III) phosphate are there in 186 grams?

Iron III phosphate is $FePO_4$

$$1Fe \times 55.9 \text{ amu/Fe} = 55.9 \text{ amu}$$

$$1P \times 31 \text{ amu/P} = 31 \text{ amu}$$

$$4O \times 16 \text{ amu/O} = 64 \text{ amu}$$

Formula weight is   150.9 amu

moles = weight/formula weight = 186 g / 150.9 g/mole = 1.23 moles

13. A somewhat strange and toxic compound was found in a cave. It has the following composition: % Fe = 41.8; % C = 26.9; % N = 31.3. What is its empirical formula?

Elem	%	%/AtWt	Div by Smallest Number
Fe	41.8	41.8/55.9 = 0.748	0.748/0.748 = 1
C	26.9	26.9/12 = 2.2	2.2/0.748 = 2.94 is about 3
N	31.3	31.3/14 = 2.2	2.2/0.748 = 2.94 is about 3

Empirical formula is FeC_3N_3 which is actually $Fe(CN)_3$

14. Another compound was found in the same cave with the main element having two isotopes- 51% isotope 178 and the remainder isotope 179. What is its atomic mass? Which of the following elements is it most likely to be Y, Hf, C, Pt?

First, since there are two isotopes and the total is 100%, then the % of the second isotope is 100 - 51 = 49%.

Atomic weight is the summation of the contributions of each isotope.

Atomic weight = 0.51 × 178 + 0.49 × 179 = 90.78 + 87.71 = 178.49 which is nearest the atomic weight of Hf of the elements given. The atomic weight for Hf is 178.49.

15. If you remove 2 electrons and 3 neutrons from Ag, what element would it be?

Since no protons are exchanged, the element is the same element, Ag.

16. What is the percentage weight of oxygen in iron II sulfate?

Iron II sulfate is $FeSO_4$

Formula weight is

$$1Fe \times 55.9 \text{ amu/Fe} = 55.9 \text{ amu}$$

$$1S \times 32 \text{ amu/S} = 32 \text{ amu}$$

$$4O \times 16 \text{ amu/O} = 64 \text{ amu}$$

Formula weight is 151.9 amu

$$\% O = (64/151.9) \times 100 = 42 \%$$

17. How many moles of titanium IV nitrate are in 150 grams?

Titanium IV nitrate is $Ti(NO_3)_4$

Formula weight

$$1Ti \times 48 \text{ amu/Ti} = 48 \text{ amu}$$

$$4N \times 14 \text{ amu/N} = 56 \text{ amu}$$

$$12O \times 16 \text{ amu/O} = 192 \text{ amu}$$

Formula weight is 296 amu or 296 g/mole

Moles = Weight/Formula weight = Weight /Gram formula weight = 150 g/296 g/mole = 0.51

18. What is the mass of one molecule of carbon tetrachloride?

First, let us determine the formula and formula weight for carbon tetrachloride since we know that the formula weight it the weight in grams of one mole and it is also the weight of Avogadro's number of carbon tetrachloride molecules.

Carbon tetrachloride is CCl_4

$$1C \times 12 \text{ amu/C} = 12 \text{ amu}$$

$$4Cl \times 35.5 \text{ amu/Cl} = 142 \text{ amu}$$

Formula weight is 154 amu

We will not solve the problem using proportions since we know that one mole, or 154 grams of carbon tetrachloride has Avogadro's number of carbon tetrachloride molecules in it or 6×10^{23}.

$$\frac{154 \text{ g}}{\times \text{ g}} = \frac{6 \times 10^{23} \text{ molecules}}{1 \text{ molecule}}$$

Cross multiple and we have that $6 \times 10^{23} \times = 154$ g and $\times = 154$ g/$6 \times 10^{23} = 26 \times 10^{-23}$ g $= 2.6 \times 10^{-22}$ g which is a very small weight and a small weight is expected because molecules are generally very small so should weight little.

19. What is the formula mass of mercury II nitrate?

$Hg(NO_3)_2$

$1Hg \times 201 \text{ amu/Hg} = 201 \text{ amu}$

$2N \times 14 \text{ amu/N} = 28 \text{ amu}$

$6O \times 16 \text{ amu/O} = 96 \text{ amu}$

Formula mass is the total or sum of the amu = 325 amu or 325 g/mole.

20. Name the following compounds:

$Zn(NO_3)_2$	zinc II nitrate
$Fe_2(SO_4)_3$	iron III sulfate
S_2Br_6	disulfur hexabromide
$Ca_3(PO_4)_2$	calcium phosphate

21. Polytetrafluoroethylene (Teflon) is made from the monomer tetrafluoroethylene which has 24% carbon and 76% fluorine. What is its empirical formula?

Elem	%	%/AtWt	Div by Smallest Number
C	24	24/12 = 2	2/2 = 1
F	76	76/19 = 4	4/2 = 2

The empirical formula is CF_2

22. How many moles are in 36 grams of water?

Water is H_2O

$2H \times 1 \, amu/H = 2 \, amu$

$1O \times 16 \, amu/O = 16 \, amu$

Formula weight is $16 + 2 = 18 \, amu = 18 \, g/mole$

moles = weight/gram formula weight = $36 \, g/18 \, g/mole = 2 \, moles$

23. How many molecules are in 36 grams of water?

From the problem above we determined that 36 grams of water contains 2 moles of water.

Number of water molecules = number of moles of water $\times$ Avogadro's number = 2 moles $\times$ 6×10^{23} water molecules/mole = 12×10^{23} = 1.2×10^{24} water molecules written in scientific notation.

24. How many atoms are in 36 grams of water?

From the previous two problems we determined that there was 2 moles of water molecules and 1.2×10^{24} water molecules. Since each water molecule contains three atoms, one oxygen atom and two hydrogen atoms, we simply multiple the number of water molecules by three.

3 atoms/water molecule $\times$ 1.2×10^{24} water molecules = 3.6×10^{24} atoms.

25. How many grams are in 0.4 moles of sodium hydroxide?

We know that the number of moles is equal to the weight divided by the gram formula weight or

moles = weight/gram formula weight, gfw, or

moles = weight/ gfw

We can restructure this to look more like a four part proportions allowing us to cross multiple.

$$\frac{moles}{1} = \frac{weight}{gfw}$$

Cross multiplication gives

weight = moles $\times$ gfw.

This is an important relationship and we simply derived it from another relationship we had memorized. We need to calculate the formula weight for sodium hydroxide, NaOH.

$1Na \times 23 \, amu/Na + 1O \times 16 \, amu/O + 1H \times 1 \, amu/H = 40 \, g/mole.$

For the current problem we have

weight = 0.4 moles $\times$ 40 g/mole = 16 g

26. In SO_2 how many oxygen molecules are there in it?

There are no, zero, oxygen molecules since the oxygen atoms are bonded to sulfur atoms and not to another oxygen atom.

27. What is the atomic weight of an element that has 70% of the isotope 43 and 30% isotope 45?

Atomic weight = $0.7 \times 43 + 0.3 \times 45 = 30.1 + 13.5 = 43.6$

28. What is the weight of one atom of carbon dioxide?

The formula for carbon dioxide is CO_2. We know that one mole of carbon dioxide, CO_2, weights one gram formula weight, 44 g/mole, and that there are 6×10^{23} CO_2 molecules in the one mole and 44 grams.

Again, we will set up a proportion that describes this situation that allows us to solve for the weight of a single CO_2 molecule.

$$\frac{44 \text{ g}}{\text{Xg}} = \frac{6 \times 10^{23} \text{ CO}_2 \text{ molecules}}{1 \text{ CO}_2 \text{ molecule}}$$

$X = 44/6 \times 10^{23} = 7.3 \times 10^{-23}$ g

29. How many moles calcium nitrate are in 60 grams of calcium nitrate?

First, we need to know the formula for calcium nitrate.

$Ca(NO_3)_2$

Next we need to know the gfwt for calcium nitrate.

1Ca $\times$ 40 amu/Ca = 40 amu

2N $\times$ 14 amu/N = 28 amu

6 O $\times$ 16 amu/O = 96 amu

Total = 164 amu = 164 g/mole

Number of moles = wt/gfw = 60 g/164 g/mole = 0.37 g.

30. What is the answer to problem 29 to two significant figures in scientific notation?

3.7×10^{-1}

SAMPLE TEST PROBLEMS

Name _____   Date _____

Circle only correct answers.

31. A gold ring weights 39.4 grams. How many molecules of gold are in the ring?

   a. 1.2×10^{23};   b. 2.4×10^{23};   c. 6×10^{23};   d. 0.2;   e. 1.

32. para-Dichlorobenzene, $C_6H_4Cl_2$, was used as a "mothball" material to keep moths out of clothing. It is a white solid. What is its formula mass?

   a. 72;   b. 96;   c. 113;   d. 132;   e. 147.

33. What is the formula weight of titanium IV nitrate?

   a. 182;   b. 226;   c. 296;   d. 326;   e. 431.

34. What is the percentage sulfur in barium sulfate?

   a. 13.7;   b. 26.3;   c. 32.1;   d. 42.3;   e. 48.9.

35. How many moles of a newly discovered molecule are in 3.6×10^{24} molecules of this material?

   a. cannot tell since you must know the structure of the molecule before you can determine the number of moles.   b. cannot tell since you must know the number of molecules in a single unit before you can give the answer.   c. 3 moles;   d. 6 moles; 12 moles.

36. Acetone is used in our chemistry laboratories as a solvent. It has 62.1 % carbon; 10.34 % hydrogen, and 27.9% oxygen. What is its empirical formula?

   a. C_4H_6O;   b. $C_8H_{12}O$;   c. C_3H_6O d. $C_4H_{12}O$ e. $C_5H_{10}O$.

37. Ethylene is a colorless gas that is employed to make a number of different polyethylene products including the grocery bags found in our stores. It has 85.71 % carbon and 14.29 % hydrogen. Its molecular weight is 28 amu or 28 grams/mole. What is its molecular formula?

   a. CH;   b. CH_2;   c. C_2H_2;   d. C_2H_4;   e. C_3H_8.

38. What is the percentage weight of sulfur in sulfur trioxide?

   a. 40;   b. 50;   c. 65;   d. 80;   e. 25.

39. Three moles of chloroform, $CHCl_3$, weights about _____ grams.

   a. 87;   b. 245;   c. 322;   d. 359;   e. 435.

40. How many moles are in 5,000 mg of chromium III phosphate?

   a. 0.034;   b. 34;   c. 0.0021;   d. 3.4   e. 0.021.

Chemical Reactions

WRITING CHEMICAL EQUATIONS

A chemical equation is the symbolic representation of a chemical reaction utilizing chemical formulas-it is a chemistry "short-hand".

$$A + B \rightarrow C + D$$

is "read" as "the reaction of A with B "goes to"
"gives"
"react to form"
"yields" C and D.

A and B are called the **REACTANTS**, the arrow is read "goes to", "react to form", "yields" or "gives" and C and D are called the **PRODUCTS**.

It is customary to write **BALANCED** equations such that the _NUMBER_ and _KIND_ of atoms appearing on the RIGHT (or reactant) side of the arrow are EQUAL (in number and kind) to those atoms that appear on the LEFT (or product) side.

COEFFICIENTS (numbers that appear before the formula weight of a material in the equation) are added to BALANCE the equation-make the number and kind of atoms (not compounds) that react be the same in number and kind as appear as products.

Thus, it is the ATOMS that are balanced-not molecules, compounds.

(Thus, for the balanced equation $2H_2 + O_2 \rightarrow 2H_2O$ the 2 in front of H_2 and H_2O is a coefficient and says that to have a balanced equation we need 2 H_2 units and 2 H_2O units. There is an understood "1" in front of the O_2 that is not written but we know that it is there. Notice that we can also write this equation by changing the order of hydrogen and oxygen as follows. $O_2 + 2H_2 \rightarrow 2H_2O$. We can also write this going in the opposite direction just as long as the products and reactants are the same. $2H_2O \leftarrow 2H_2 + O_2$.)

Further, the "form" or "phase" of the reactants and products may also be indicated where (g) = gas; (l) = liquid, (s) = solid, and (aq) indicates an aqueous (water) solution.

Thus, for the reaction of diatomic (contains TWO atoms of oxygen) oxygen gas and diatomic (contains TWO atoms of hydrogen) hydrogen gas to form gaseous water we have

$$O_2 + H_2 \rightarrow H_2O$$

as the "unbalanced" equation where

"O_2" and "H_2" are REACTANTS and the "H_2O" is the PRODUCT.

We can "BALANCE" the reaction by placing a "2" in front of "H_2" and in front of "H_2O". Since "O_2" appears in the balanced equation only once, by agreement, we "understand" that a "1" is there and do not place the "1" in the equation.

Thus the "completed" equation (including the phases) is as follows:

$$O_2\,(g) + 2H_2\,(g) \rightarrow 2H_2O\,(g)$$

Practice "balancing" and writing equations. This is a skill that will be required throughout your chemistry classes-as well as other classes that include chemical reactions.

Lets practice balancing some reactions. To do this we will simply put the equation and then the balanced equation later.

$$C_2H_6 + O_2 \rightarrow CO_2 + H_2O$$

This is an example of a combustion or burning reaction of hydrocarbons, materials with only hydrogen and carbon in them. The products are carbon dioxide and water. The major products are also carbon dioxide and water for compounds that contain only C, H, and O such as sugars, wood, and paper.

The almost balanced reaction is

$$C_2H_6 + 3.5\,O_2 \rightarrow 2\,CO_2 + 3\,H_2O$$

Balanced reactions must have whole numbers in front of each compound or element. Where there is only one we do not place a one but it is understood to be there. Here we have a 3.5 in front of the O_2. We can get rid of the fraction by simply multiplying by two giving us

$$2\,C_2H_6 + 7\,O_2 \rightarrow 4\,CO_2 + 6\,H_2O$$

This is now a balanced reaction.

We might view

$$4\,C_2H_6 + 14\,O_2 \rightarrow 8\,CO_2 + 12\,H_2O$$

as a balanced reaction since there are no fractions but it is not because we can divide everything by two and get whole numbers.

Thus, a balanced reaction must have only whole numbers and be the smallest combination of small whole numbers.

What is balanced in a chemical equation? It is the **number** of each kind of element that is balanced.

Let us try

$$K + O_2 \rightarrow K_2O$$

The balanced reaction is

$$4\,K + O_2 \rightarrow 2\,K_2O$$

AQUEOUS SOLUBILITY

A **solution** contains a **solute** and **solvent**. For instance, common table salt, NaCl, dissolves in water forming sodium ions and chloride ions. Solutions that have water as the solvent are called **aqueous** solutions.

Solutes that dissolve producing ions are called **electrolytes**. Those that produce lots of ions such as NaCl are called **strong electrolytes**. Those that produce only a few ions such as acetic acid are called **weak electrolytes**. And, those that produce no ions either because they are covalently bonded such as sugar or because they are not soluble in water are called **non-electrolytes**. Those solutes that dissolve are said to be **soluble** and those that do not dissolve to an appreciable extent are called **insoluble**. When a material is formed within a solution and that material is not soluble, it falls out from solution, it **precipitates** from solution.

We will use a table, Table 7.1, that contains which compounds are soluble or not soluble (insoluble) to help us in predicting if an ionic compound is soluble. You will need to memorize it and be able to predict what compounds are soluble or not soluble.

Table 7.1 *Solubility Rules in Water*

Compounds that contain the following ions are mostly SOLUBLE.	Exceptions
Li^{+1}, Na^{+1}, K^{+1}, Rb^{+1}, NH_4^{+1} (Hint-these are Group IA ions plus NH_4^{+1})	None
NO_3^{-1}, $C_2H_3O_2^{-1}$	None
Cl^{-1}, Br^{-1}, I^{-1} (Hint-Group VIIA ions)	When combined with Ag^{+1}, Hg^{+1}, Pb^{+2} compound is not soluble
SO_4^{-2}	When combined with Sr^{+2}, Ba^{+2}, Ca^{+2}, Pb^{+2} compound not soluble
	(Hint-mostly Group IIA)
Compounds containing the following ions are mostly INSOLUBLE.	Exceptions
OH^{-1}, S^{-2}	When combined with Li^{+1}, Na^{+1}, K^{+1}, Rb^{+1}, NH_4^{+1} (Hint-Group IA)
	When combined with Sr^{+2}, Ba^{+2}, Ca^{+2} soluble
CO_3^{-2}, PO_4^{-3}	When combined with Li^{+1}, Na^{+1}, K^{+1}, Rb^{+1}, NH_4^{+1} (Group IA)

Be able to predict the solubility when given a compound.

PREDICTING PRECIPITATION REACTIONS

For the addition of an aqueous solution of sodium bromide to an aqueous solution of silver nitrate we have

$$NaBr + AgNO_3 \rightarrow$$

We need to see what possible combinations of cations and anions are to complete the "products" side of the equation. Here there are four possible combinations of a cation and an anion. Two have already been given, NaBr and $AgNO_3$. From the solubility table we see that both NaBr and $AgNO_3$ are soluble. The other combinations are $NaNO_3$ which is a sodium salt so it is soluble. The other combination is AgBr.

$$NaBr + AgNO_3 \rightarrow NaNO_3 + AgBr \text{ (s)}$$

We see that halides such as Br^{-1} are generally soluble but with some exceptions and one exception is when combined with Ag^{+1}. Thus, AgBr is not soluble and we will have a precipitation of the AgBr since it is not soluble. We often add the symbol (s) to indicate that the material is not soluble.

Let us look at what occurs when aqueous solutions of sodium phosphate and iron (III) nitrate are added together. From the solubility table we see that all alkaline metal compounds are soluble and sodium is an alkaline metal so that sodium phosphate is soluble. From the table we also see that all nitrates are soluble so iron (III) nitrate is soluble in water. Again, we simply identify the four possible combinations of cations and anions. Two are already given as the original salts added to the solution. The other two possible simple combinations are sodium nitrate, which according to the solubility table is soluble and iron (III) phosphate which is not soluble according to the solubility table. The final equation is then:

$$Na_3PO_4 + Fe(NO_3)_3 \rightarrow 3NaNO_3 + FePO_4 \text{ (s)}$$

MOLECULAR AND IONIC EQUATIONS

MOLECULAR EQUATIONS-where the substances are written as if they were molecular in nature even though they may actually exist in solution as ions. Here, descriptions such as (s) indicate that the material is not soluble and (aq) indicating that the material is soluble in water.

$$CaCl_2(aq) + Na_2CO_3(aq) \rightarrow CaCO_3(s) + 2NaCl(aq)$$

IONIC EQUATIONS-where all the compounds that form ions in aqueous solution are written as ions. Since acetic acid is a weak acid it is NOT written as an ionic species and as a solid that is not soluble, like AgCl , does not form ionic species it is also not written as an ion. By comparison, HCl is a strong acid and does appreciably form ions in solution so it is written as ions. NaCl is a soluble salt, so it forms ions when dissolved in water.

$$Ca^{+2} + 2Cl^- + 2Na^+ + CO_3^{-2} \rightarrow CaCO_3 \text{ (s)} + 2Na^+ + 2Cl^-$$

NET IONIC EQUATIONS-where dissolved ions that are NOT involved (that is, they are not changed from each side of the arrow "—>") in the reaction are OMITTED.

$$Ca^{+2} + CO_3^{-2} \rightarrow CaCO_3 \text{ (s)}$$

Ions such as $Na+$, OH^- are not changed in the chemical reaction and are called **SPECTATOR IONS**. Such "Spectator Ions" are INCLUDED in the MOLECULAR and IONIC equations but ELIMINATED in NET IONIC equations.

ACIDS-BASES

Arrhenius defined an **acid** as a substance that increases the acidity, proton, hydrogen ion, or hydronium content of an aqueous (water) solution when dissolved. These three names refer to the same thing- proton, hydrogen ion, hydronium ion (H_3O^+; a protonated water molecule).

$$HA \rightarrow H^+ + A^-$$

An Arrhenius **base** is defined as a substance that increases the basicity or hydroxide content of the aqueous solution when it is dissolved in water.

$$BOH \rightarrow B^+ + OH^-$$

The terms STRONG ACID, WEAK ACID and STRONG BASE, WEAK BASE are directly measurable using conductivity as discussed in the next section. A **strong acid** largely dissociates, ionizes, forming ions upon dissolving in water giving a relatively large quantity of protons; a **weak acid** dissolves in water but forms only a small proportion of protons. By comparison, a strong base almost totally dissociates when dissolved in water giving a relatively large quantity of hydroxide ions. A weak base dissolves in water giving only a few ions and a few hydroxide ions.

Thus, nitric acid is an acid since it increases the hydrogen ion, etc. content when dissolved in water.

$$HNO_3 \rightarrow H^+ + NO_3^{-1}$$

It is said to be a strong acid because essentially every nitric acid molecule ionizes, forms ions, when dissolved in water; essentially every nitric acid molecule dissolves forming a proton and a nitrate ion. It is also called a strong electrolyte.

We need to know common weak/strong acids/bases.

The strong acids we need to memorize are as follows:

Nitric acid, HNO_3
Sulfuric acid, H_2SO_4
Perchloric acid, $HClO_4$
and the HX (X =halogen) such as HCl; HBr; HI but not HF.

As noted elsewhere, strong acids are also strong electrolytes.

There are many other acids but for now we will consider them weak acids. Weak acids include acetic acid, carbonic acid, phosphoric acid, and oxalic acid.

Bases, according to Arrhenius, are compounds that when added to water increase the concentration of the hydroxide, OH^{-1}, ion. Thus, sodium hydroxide is a base since it gives an increase in the hydroxide ion when it is dissolved in water.

$$NaOH \rightarrow Na^+ + OH^{-1}$$

Sodium hydroxide is a strong base since it gives essentially one OH^{-1} for each sodium hydroxide dissolved. It is also a strong electrolyte. Strong bases are mainly the hydroxides of Group IA and IIA metals such as KOH, and $Ba(OH)_2$. Metal compounds containing the hydroxide, OH^{-1}, unit are bases. But there are lots of materials that contain OH groups that are not bases such as most sugars and alcohols. Thus, only materials that contain the OH group bonded to a metal atom are bases for our present discussion.

ACID RAIN

Acid rain is the result of the formation of acids from the reaction of sulfur oxides and nitrogen oxides with water.

Sulfur Trioxide + Water → Sulfuric Acid

$$SO_3 + H_2O \rightarrow H_2SO_4$$

Nitrogen Dioxide + Water → Nitric Acid + Nitrous Acid

$$2NO + H_2O \rightarrow HNO_3 + HNO_2$$

NEUTRALIZATION REACTIONS

Acids and bases react to give a salt and water. They do so until all of the acid or base is used up. Thus, the proton from the acid "neutralizes" the hydroxide from the base and this reaction is known as a neutralization reaction. This is a general reaction and one that you should remember.

$$Acid + Base \rightarrow Salt + H_2O$$

The reaction of the $H^+ + OH^{-1}$ is the net reaction and the product is H_2O

$$HCl + NaOH \rightarrow NaCl + H_2O$$

Let us again write a series of equations for some reactions between acids and bases.

The molecular equation for the reaction between potassium hydroxide and nitric acid is as follows remembering that the product of the reaction between an acid and base is a salt and water.

$$KOH + HNO_3 \rightarrow KNO_3 + H_2O$$

The ionic equation is

$$K^+ + OH^- + H^+ + NO_3^- \rightarrow K^+ + NO_3^- + H_2O$$

We remember that both potassium hydroxide and nitric acid are strong bases/acids so they are written as being ionized. The salt is also soluble according to the solubility table. Thus, the salt is also written as being ionized. Water is not appreciably ionized and so is written as being unionized.

For the net ionic equation we see that K^+ and NO_3^- are the same on both side of the reaction arrow so are spectator ions. The net ionic equation is the formation of water.

$$H^+ + OH^- \rightarrow H_2O$$

Let us now look at what this series of reactions looks like for the reaction of a weak acid acetic acid and a weak base, ammonium hydroxide. The molecular equation is as follows.

$$NH_4OH + HC_2H_3O_2 \rightarrow NH_4C_2H_3O_2 + H_2O$$

The ionic reaction is as follows. Note that because the acid and base are weak they are written as being unionized. Ammonium acetate is soluble in water according to the solubility table and is ionized so it is written as such.

$$NH_4OH + HC_2H_3O_2 \rightarrow NH_4^+ + C_2H_3O_2^- + H_2O$$

Finally, the net ionic equation is the same as the ionic equation with no spectator ions because all of the species on the reaction side are different than what appears on the product side.

Many of us have acid reflux caused by the presence of excess acid. Acid, HCl, is necessary to help digest food in our stomach but excess acid can make us uncomfortable. Depending on the extent of discomfort and location we call this acid reflux, heartburn, etc. Many of the early acid reflux chemical treatments used weak bases or materials that resulted in minimizing the acidity in the stomach and surrounding areas. These include weak bases such as $Mg(OH)_2$ present in milk of magnesia and $Al(OH)_3$ contained in Mylanta; and $CaCO_3$ (chalk) contained in Tums that acts to moderate acidity.

IONIZATION

We will us an apparatus such as shown below, where the light bulb will only glow when the current is connected, to illustrate the concept of ionization. The current is connected when ions flow from one electrode to the other electrode thus completing the current and allowing the light bulb to glow. Ions are formed only when the added compound is soluble and forms ions. The solvent is water.

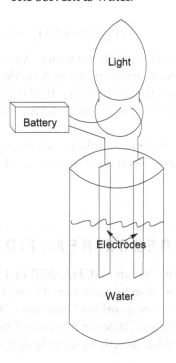

Let us first add a spoonful of sodium chloride to the water. The light bulb glows. It glows because sodium chloride dissolves in water forming ions, essentially 100%. We say that sodium chloride is then essentially totally ionized. NaCl is called an electrolyte since it dissolves and forms ions. Since it is essentially totally ionized it is referred to as a **strong electrolyte**. Thus, the first requirement to be an **electrolyte** is that a material forms ions when dissolved.

$$NaCl \rightarrow Na^+ + Cl^-$$

We next add some common sugar. The sugar dissolves but does not form ions and the light bulb remains dark. Sugar is a **non-electrolyte**. Thus, having a material soluble is not sufficient to make it an electrolyte. Again, it must form ions.

Ionic compounds often form ions. Sodium chloride is an ionic compound and forms lots of ions and is an electrolyte.

Next, we will add AgCl. Silver chloride is an ionic compound but the light does not turn on because while silver chloride is ionic, it is not soluble in water. (Remember the solubility table.) It too is a non-electrolyte.

Next we add sodium hydroxide. The light burns brightly. Sodium hydroxide is a base and it dissociates essentially totally forming ions. It is then a strong electrolyte. From our discussion of bases, we know that NaOH is a **strong base** because it ionizes essentially totally forming the sodium cation and the hydroxide anion.

$$NaOH \rightarrow Na^+ + OH^-$$

HCl is added to the water and again the light burns brightly because HCl almost completely ionizes. From our discussion of acids, we know that HCl is an acid. Because it ionizes almost completely it is a strong electrolyte and **strong acid**.

Next, we add NH_4OH to the water. The light bulb dimly lights up. This is because, while ammonium hydroxide ionizes some, it ionizes only a little such that for every about 10,000 NH_4OH only one forms ions. We call such a substance a **weak electrolyte** and since it is a base, a **weak base**.

$$NH_4OH \rightarrow NH_4^+ + OH^-$$

We next add acetic acid to the water. Again, the light bulb dimly lights up. As in the case with ammonium hydroxide, acetic acid ionizes to a very limited extent, again for about every 10,000 acetic acid molecules added to the water, only one ionizes. Acetic acid is referred to as a weak electrolyte and a **weak acid**.

Thus, we have become familiar with a number of terms including electrolyte, strong/weak electrolyte, non-electrolyte, and strong/weak acid/base.

OXIDATION-REDUCTION OR REDOX REACTIONS

Redox reactions involve an EXCHANGE of ELECTRONS. Where there is oxidation there must also be reduction. We will see that the terms associated with redox reactions are a series of opposites. To help remember the definitions we can use the oxidation or reaction of iron with oxygen. This, in fact was the basis of redox reactions so it is appropriate that we use it as an example.

Before we return to this let us see how we determine the oxidation number. We determined oxidation when we were naming the transition compounds.

We assign oxidation numbers according to some rules that are related to the chemical tendencies and placement within the periodic chart of the specific atoms. These rules allow us to assign what is called an **OXIDATION NUMBER** to atoms within a compound. These rules are as follows:

1. Oxidation number of an element in the elementary state is zero. Fe, O_2, Al, Xe, Cl_2

2. Oxidation number of a charged cation or anion is the charge on the cation or anion. $Na^+ = +1$, $Ba^{+2} = +2$, $Cl^- = -1$, $Fe^{+2} = 2$, $H^+ = +1$

3. In almost all compounds Halides$= -1$, Group IA (alkaline metals)$= +1$, Group IIA (alkaline earths) $=+2$, H $= +1$, O $= -2$

4. Sum of all oxidation numbers is the charge on the species-if neutral then zero, or charged species it is the net charge of the species.
   We will practice calculating oxidation numbers for a number of situations. Examples-

   $HClO_3$ H $= +1$, O $= -2$/each; therefore Cl $= 6 - 1 = 5$

$KMnO_4$ MnO_2

K_2CrO_4 CrO CrO_2 CrO_3 $K_2Cr_2O_7$

H_3PO_4 H_3PO_3 P_4O_{10} P_4O_6

H_2SO_4 H_2SO_3 H_2S SO_2 SO_3

NO NO_2 N_2O_4 HNO_3 HNO_2

$FeCl_2$ $FeCl_3$

$CuCl_2$ Cu_2Cl_2

$CaNaPO_4$ $NaHCO_3$ SO_4^{-2} ClO_4^{-1}

CH_4 CH_3Cl CH_2Cl_2 $CHCl_3$ CCl_4 CO_2 CO C

Now we return to our reaction of iron with oxygen to form iron (II) oxide, FeO.

$$2Fe + O_2 \rightarrow 2FeO$$

The oxidation number for Fe is zero, for O_2 is zero and for Fe in FeO it is +2, because the oxidation number of oxygen in a compound is usually −2 and the net charge for FeO is zero. We see that the oxidation number for iron has increased from 0 to +2 as it changed from metallic Fe on the left side of the equation to FeO on the product side of the equation. We agree to call such an increased oxidation number from reactant to product oxidation. Iron then has been oxidized, reacted with oxygen. So in oxidation there is an increase in oxidation number. Conversely, the oxidation number of O has decreased from 0 to −2. Reduction is then a decrease in oxidation number. This is our first opposite.

Now, let us divide the equation into two **half cells**, one dealing with oxidation and one dealing with reduction. The oxidation half cell is then

$$Fe \rightarrow Fe^{+2}$$

To balance this half cell we need to have the charge be the same on each side of the arrow. To do this we add two electrons to the product side giving

$$Fe \rightarrow Fe^{+2} + 2e^-$$

Thus, iron as lost two electrons to become Fe^{+2}. Overall, for each increase or loss of oxidation number there will be a loss or gain in one electron. Thus, in oxidation there is a loss in electrons.

For oxygen we have the reduction half cell.

$$O_2 \rightarrow 2O^{-2}$$

Or a decrease in two oxidation numbers for each oxygen atom for a total change of 4 oxidation number change. Again, for the reactant and product side to be balanced we need the charges to be the same, not necessarily zero. For this to occur we can add four electrons to the reactant side giving

$$4e^- + O_2 \rightarrow 2O^{-2}$$

Thus, in reduction there is a gain in electrons.

Another set of opposites. For oxidation there is an increase in oxidation number but a decrease in electrons. For reduction there is a decrease in oxidation number but an increase in electrons.

Finally, our last set of opposites. An oxidizing agent is the material that has been reduced, here oxygen, while the reducing agent is the material that has been oxidized, here iron.

Summary

OXIDATION	REDUCTION
Increased oxidation number	**Decreased oxidation number**
Loss in electrons	**Gain in electrons**
Called reducing agent	**Called oxidizing agent**
But	**But**
It is oxidized	**It is reduced**

For the reaction of calcium with chlorine gas we have

$$2Ca + Cl_2 \rightarrow 2CaCl_2$$

OXIDATION-is defined as a gain in oxidation or loss in electrons.

$$Ca \rightarrow Ca^{+2} + 2e^-$$

Here calcium increases its oxidation number from zero to plus two and this is caused because of the loss of two electrons. The reaction of calcium metal going to calcium plus two ion is called OXIDATION and the chemical that causes or brings about this loss in electrons is called an OXIDIZING AGENT because it is the "agent" or cause of the elemental calcium losing its electrons. Here, the oxidizing agent is chlorine gas.

REDUCTION-is the opposite of OXIDATION and is defined as the LOSS in

oxidation number or the GAIN in electrons. For our reaction between calcium and chlorine we have for the half cell

$$Cl_2 + 2e^- \rightarrow 2Cl^-$$

Thus, Cl_2 decreases, lowers its oxidation number from zero to minus one per chlorine atom. Chlorine is said to be REDUCED and it has been reduced by an agent or chemical that supplies the needed electrons. The agent that supplies these electrons is called an REDUCING AGENT and is calcium.

If the two reactions cited above were brought together, Ca would be said to be OXIDIZED by Cl_2 which would be called the OXIDIZING AGENT. Similarly, Cl_2 would be said to be REDUCED and the agent or cause of this reduction or gain in electrons (that is the chemical that supplied the necessary electrons) is Ca and it is then called the REDUCING AGENT.

Of interest, when asked **what is the reducing/oxidizing agent, who loses/gains electrons and who gains/loses electrons the answer always is on the product side**, never on the product side.

COMBUSTION REACTIONS   Combustion reactions are a group of redox reactions. In **combustion** reactions with hydrocarbons and materials that contain only C, H, and O the main products are **carbon dioxide** and **water**. Another term sometimes employed when describing combustion reactions is "burning."

Thus, the combustion or burning products of methane and oxygen are carbon dioxide and water.

$$CH_4 + O_2 \rightarrow CO_2 + H_2O$$

Practice balancing combustion reactions such as these. For methane the balanced reaction is

$$CH_4 + 2O_2 \rightarrow CO_2 + 2H_2O$$

Here, carbon in methane has an oxidation number of -4 since each hydrogen is a plus 1. The oxidation number in carbon for carbon dioxide is $+4$ so that carbon has increased its oxidation number from -4 to $+4$. Thus, we say that methane, CH_4, has been oxidized. Notice we do not say that carbon has been oxidized but rather the reactant that contains the carbon has been oxidized. Remembering that oxidation is a gain in oxidation number, we say that methane has been oxidized, it has gained in oxidation number and lost electrons and is the reducing agent. Oxygen has changed its oxidation number from a zero in O_2 to a -2 in CO_2. Again, using our system of opposites we can say that O_2 is reduced because it has a decrease in oxidation number from zero to -2; gained electrons, and is a oxidizing agent.

WHY REACTIONS ARE DRIVEN TO OCCUR

ELEMENTARY MY DEAR DR. WATSON (all in an aqueous environment).

A. **FORMATION OF A PRECIPITATE**-The formation of a material that is not soluble in the reaction solution generally drives reactions to completion. This includes the formation of a precipitate or gas. To be able to correctly "predict" or identify which set of compounds will produce a precipitate, we need to know the general solubility of common ionic compounds. The solubility table gives a brief description of such compounds and should be memorized.

INSOLUBLE and INSOLUBILITY are relative terms that also require designating the LIQUID or SOLVENT. Here we will be talking about water-but our water-intense solution could be acidic, basic or neutral.

Some reactions "will not go" or do not occur. The addition of an aqueous solution of sodium chloride and potassium bromide simply gives us a solution that contains Na^+, K^+, Cl^-, and Br^- ions with no net reaction. From the solubility table we see that all four possible combinations of cations with anions are all soluble in aqueous solutions.

B. **NEUTRALIZATION REACTIONS**-reaction of an acid and a base gives a salt and water. The driving force for these types of reaction is said to be the formation of a molecular compound, here water.

We can write the acid portion as H^+ or as a hydronium, H_3O^+, ion.

Some neutralization reactions are a bit more complex and occur in stages. Thus reaction of phosphoric acid with sodium hydroxide occurs giving a complex of products-always a salt and water-the proportion of products are dependent on the relative amounts of sodium hydroxide and phosphoric acid.

$$NaOH + H_3PO_4 \rightarrow NaH_2PO_4 \rightarrow Na_2HPO_4 \rightarrow Na_3PO_4$$

C. **EXCHANGE OF ELECTRONS-REDOX REACTIONS** The driving force for redox reactions is the exchange of electrons resulting in oxidation/reduction occurring.

D. **GAS FORMATION** As noted before, formation of an insoluble material drives reactions to completion. This insoluble material can be a solid or gas. An example is the reaction of sulfuric with lithium sulfide forming gaseous hydrosulfide and lithium sulfate.

$$H_2SO_4 + Li_2S \rightarrow Li_2SO_4 + H_2S \text{ (g)}$$

In certain reactions the formation of a gas may occur in a two step process. Thus, while carbonic acid has some solubility in water, when its solubility is exceeded, carbonic acid decomposed into water and carbon dioxide gas.

$$HCl + NaHCO_3 \rightarrow H_2CO_3 + NaCl \text{ and}$$

$$H_2CO_3 \rightarrow H_2O + CO_2 \text{ (g)}$$

One of the techniques to drive plastic submarines was to fill the hollow part of the submarine with baking soda (sodium bicarbonate) sodium hydrogen carbonate and to add several drops of vinegar which contains acetic acid. A cap was placed on the top of the submarine mixture and as the reaction occurred carbon dioxide is formed and forced through a hole in the tail end of the plastic submarine propelling the submarine forward. One beauty of this mixture is that most homes have the chemical ingredients readily available. Another positive is that the ingredients are relatively harmless.

$$HC_2H_3O_2 + NaHCO_3 \rightarrow H_2CO_3 + NaC_2H_3O \rightarrow H_2O + CO_2 \text{ (g)} + NaC_2H_3O_2$$

REACTION RATES

Reaction rates tell about the speed of reactions; they tell us how fast reactants are used up and products are formed. Reaction rates increase with increase in temperature. For a reaction to occur there must be sufficient energy. The energy barrier needed to be overcome, the barrier to getting the reactants to change into products, is called the **activation energy** or **energy of activation**. Thus, to get H_2 and O_2 to react forming H_2O sufficient energy must be available to push them together allowing the H-H and O-O bonds to break and reform to give H-O-H bonds. **Reaction rate increases as temperature increases** since increased temperature means that more of the reactants will have sufficient energy to get over the activation energy barrier. Conversely, reaction rate decreases as temperature decreases. This is another example of a direct relationship.

To react the molecules must come into contact, often 10^{10} times or more and they must be in the right geometry. Thus, **reaction rates also increase as the concentration of reactants increase**. Catalysts generally place molecules in the right geometry acting to lower the overall activation energy.

Reactions are either net **exothermic**, giving off energy like the burning of natural gases and petroleum products, or **endothermic**, taking in a net amount of energy (cold packs). Below are two "reaction profiles." The one on the left is for an endothermic reaction and the one on the right is for an exothermic reaction. The heat of reaction which tells if it is exothermic or endothermic is the potential energy difference between the reactants and products. If the potential energy for the products is above that of the reactants, then the reaction is endothermic; conversely, if the potential energy for the products is below that of the reactants, then the reaction is exothermic and a net amount of energy is given off.

The energy difference between the reactants and the activation state is called the **activation energy** or **energy of activation**. The reaction rate or

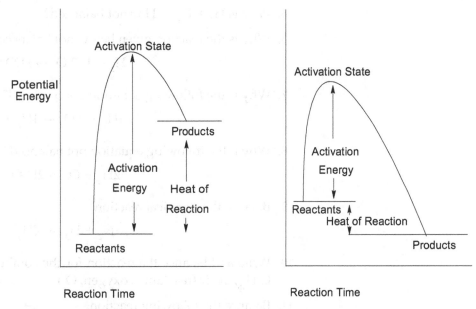

Figure 7.1 *Reaction profiles showing activation energies and heats of reaction.*

speed of a reaction is related to the activation energy. In general, if the activation energy is relatively low or small, the reaction will be fast or rapid; conversely, if the activation energy is relatively high or great, the reaction will be slow. The relationship is called an exponential relationship so that small activation energy differences are reflected in large changes in the rate.

The rate of a reaction is related to the amount of energy or heat available. As the energy available to run a reaction becomes greater, more molecules will have the necessary energy to overcome the activation energy and the faster the reaction. Again, the relationship between reaction rate and temperature is exponential so that relatively small temperature variations will greatly influence the rate.

Enzymes are proteins that are natural catalysts. They lower the energy of activation through assuring the correct geometry (orientation) as well as holding the reactants in the general vicinity of one another so that they do not have to "find" one another. These catalysts can have a phenomenal affect on the reaction rate. One reaction takes about a billion years to occur but in the presence of the correct catalysts occurs in picoseconds, an increase in about 10^{17}.

PROBLEMS

1. For the chemical reaction between nitrogen, hydrogen forming ammonium shown below (not balanced) what is the product(s) and what is(are) the reactant(s)?

$$N_2 + H_2 \rightarrow NH_3$$

2. What does the $\rightarrow$ mean in chemical reactions?

3. In a balanced reaction what is balanced?

4. What constitutes a balanced equation?

5. Why is $H_2 + O_2 \rightarrow H_2O$ not balanced?

6. Why is the reaction given below not balanced?

$$H_2 + 1/2\,O_2 \rightarrow H_2O$$

7. Why is the following equation not balanced?

$$4H_2 + 2\,O_2 \rightarrow 4H_2O$$

8. Why it the following equation not balanced?

$$2H_2 + O_2 \rightarrow 2H_2O$$

9. Balance the chemical reaction

$$N_2 + H_2 \rightarrow NH_3$$

10. Write and balance the reaction for the combustion (burning) of octane, C_8H_{18}, in air (reactant is oxygen, O_2).

11. Balance the following reaction.

$$HCl + O_2 \rightarrow H_2O + Cl_2$$

12. The reaction between an acid and base forms water and a salt and is exothermic. Write the reaction between sodium hydroxide and hydrochloric acid and show which side of the equation the heat or energy is.

$$NaOH + HCl \rightarrow NaCl + H_2O$$

13. Write a balanced equation for the reaction between nitrogen and oxygen forming nitrogen monooxide. It is an endothermic equation.

14. Write the molecular, ionic and net reaction for the reaction between ammonium hydroxide and sulfuric acid. Identify the spectator ions.

15. Write the molecular, ionic and net reaction for the reaction between potassium hydroxide and hydrobromic acid. Identify the spectator ions.

16. Write the molecular, ionic and net reaction for the reaction between iron III nitrate and potassium phosphate. Identify the spectator ions.

17. Which of the following is **not** a strong acid?

HI	Nitric acid
Sulfuric acid	Acetic acid

18. Which is **not** a strong electrolyte?

AgBr

NaOH

$FePO_4$

NaI

19. In an aqueous solution of sodium carbonate the addition of which will cause the formation of a precipitate and what is the formula of the precipitate?

$Sr(NO_3)_2$

NaI

20. What is the oxidation number of chromium in $K_2Cr_2O_7$ and $CrCl_3$?

21. What is the oxidation number of tin in $SnCl_2$ and $SnCl_4$?

22. What is oxidized and reduced, losing and gaining electrons, and reducting agent and oxidizing agent in the following equation.

$$K_2Cr_2O_7 + SnCl_2 + HCl \rightarrow CrCl_3 + SnCl_4 + H_2O + KCl$$

23. What is the oxidation number of iron in FeS and in $FeCl_3$?

24. What is the oxidation number of nitrogen in HNO_3 and NO?

25. In the following reaction which is oxidized, reduced, losing and gaining electrons, and an oxidizing and reducing agent?

$$FeS + KCl + HNO_3 \rightarrow NO + K_2SO_4 + FeCl_3 + H_2O$$

26. To balance the combustion of methane, CH_4, what should be placed in front of the oxygen molecule.

27. What is the oxidation numbers of all of the elements in potassium phosphate?

28. What is the oxidation number for Fe in $FeBr_2$?

29. Make bold only those compounds that are **strong** electrolytes.
    $PbSO_4$
    HNO_3
    KOH

30. Make bold only those compounds that are **strong** electrolytes.
    Sugar
    NH_4OH
    Citric Acid

31. What is the oxidation number of each element in the following?
    CuCl
    NaOH
    H_2S

32. A leprechaun is suspected of being a terrorist and hording precious metals. The CIA break into his home and in the basement finds two 55 gallon drums. The labels are found on the ground- potassium nitrate and silver nitrate. Using simple chemicals found in the home, how can the agents differentiate between the contents of the two drums? Is the evidence consistent with the leprechaun possibly being a terrorist and hording precious metals?

33. Which of the following is a **strong** acid?
    KOH
    LiOH
    HBr

34. Which of the following is a strong base **OR** strong acid?
    $Ca(OH)_2$
    Phosphoric acid
    Acetic acid

35. Which of the following are water soluble?
    Sodium phosphate
    Silver phosphate
    Disulfur trioxide

36. Which of the following are water soluble?
    Aluminum acetate
    Titanium nitrate
    Platinum sulfate

37. Which of the following are water soluble?
    Barium sulfate
    $V(NO_3)_2$
    $CrSO_4$

38. Which of the following are water soluble?
    BaS
    $FeSO_4$
    $CaCO_3$

39. To balance the following simple redox half cell how many electrons must be added/taken away?

$$Na \rightarrow Na^+$$

40. In problem 39 is this an oxidation or reduction half cell?

41. To balance the following redox half cell how many electrons must be added/taken away? Is this an oxidation or reduction half cell?

$$2Cl^- \rightarrow Cl_2$$

42. For the half cell

$$MnO_4^- \rightarrow MnO$$

how many water molecules must be added/ taken away in the balanced half cell occurring under acidic (acid) conditions.

43. What is the hallmark of a strong acid?

44. What is the hallmark of a strong electrolyte?

45. Which of the following forms the largest number of ions from addition of one mole to ten liters of water?
    Na_3PO_4
    NaOH
    AgI
    $CaCl_2$

46. For the below potential energy profile identify what the products and reactants are.

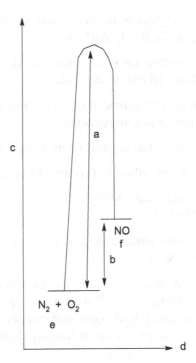

47. For the potential energy profile given in problem 46 what is a?

48. For the potential energy profile given in problem 46 what is b?

49. For the reaction potential energy profile given in problem 46 is the reaction exothermic or endothermic? Why?

50. Write the balanced equation for the reaction described in problem 46 including which side the net heat will occur.

51. If you are holding onto a beaker that has a highly endothermic reaction occurring in it, what evidence will you have that the reaction is endothermic?

52. Which of the following is a **strong** base? NaOH, LiOH, Ca(OH)$_2$, HCl, CaCl$_2$.

53. What is the connection between strong acids and bases and strong electrolytes?

54. BaSO$_4$ is ionic and yet it is not an electrolyte. Why?

55. Write the ionic equation for Na$_3$PO$_4$ in water.

56. Which of the following are **not** soluble in water? KOH, K$_2$S, PbS, (NH$_4$)$_3$PO$_4$, Ti(CO$_3$)$_2$.

57. Why does the solubility of most compounds increase when heated?

58. If you have a solution of NaNO$_3$ which of the following soluble chlorides will form a precipitate when added to the solution. Ca^{+2}, Ni^{+2}, Fe^{+2}, Co^{+2}.

59. When solutions of silver nitrate and potassium iodide are brought together a _____ reaction occurs forming _____ as a solid.

60. Which of the following will produce the greatest amount of ions? $Ca_3(PO_4)_2$, $NaCl$, $BaCl_2$, $Al(NO_3)_3$.

61. Write the reaction for vanadium V oxide reacting with hydrogen forming vanadium III oxide and water.

62. What is undergoing oxidation in the reaction described in question 61? What is undergoing reduction?

63. In problem 61 what is gaining electrons? What is the oxidizing agent?

64. The reaction described in problem 61 is a(n) _____ reaction.

65. Write the molecular, ionic and net ionic reaction that occurs between HCl and $Pb(NO_3)_2$.

66. Write the molecular, ionic and net ionic reaction that occurs between $NaBr$ and $LiNO_3$.

67. We generally write the reaction that occurs between hydrogen and oxygen forming water. But in a process called electrolysis we break up water forming hydrogen and oxygen. Write both reactions clearly showing the products from having them on the pointed side of the arrow.

68. Give three examples of salts that are soluble in water.

69. The formation of water from hydrogen and oxygen and the combustion of hydrocarbons forming carbon dioxide and water are examples of _____ reactions.

70. Balance the combustion reaction between ethane, C_2H_6 , and oxygen.

71. What is the hallmark of a **weak** base?

72. To recover iron from its oxides carbon is used. The equation for the recovery from iron III oxide is below.

$$Fe_2O_3 + C \rightarrow Fe + CO$$

What is the oxidation numbers for carbon in C and in CO?

73. In problem 72 what is oxidized and what is reduced?

74. Copper metal is dissolved in the presence of nitric acid according to the following reaction.

$$Cu + NO_3^- \rightarrow Cu^{+2} + NO_2$$

What is oxidized and what is reduced in this process?

75. Write the balanced oxidation half-cell for problem 74.

76. Write the balanced reduction half-cell for problem 74.

77. Using the half-cells derived in problems 75 and 76 balance the equation given in problem 74.

78. The reaction between tin +2 and the permanganate ion is described as follows.

$$Sn^{+2} + MnO_4^- \rightarrow Sn^{+4} + Mn^{+2}$$

What is oxidized and what is reduced?

79. Write the balanced reduction half-cell for the equation given in problem 78.

80. Write the balanced oxidation half-cell for the equation given in problem 78.

81. Balance the equation given in problem 78.

82. Our automobiles often require a battery to start the engine. The most common battery is called the lead storage battery. The energy to start the engine is supplied by the exchange of electrons in the battery. The balanced redox reaction is described as follows.

$$Pb + PbO_2 + 2H_2SO_4 \rightarrow 2PbSO_4 + 2H_2O$$

What is oxidized and what is reduced?

83. The reaction described in problem 82 occurs in sulfuric acid which is called the battery acid. Sulfuric acid is a strong/weak electrolyte and a strong/weak acid. Underline the correct term.

In automobiles, the alternator allows the battery to be recharged so that the battery life is extended from a few starts to thousands of starts. The equation describing the recharging is simply the reverse reaction. Knowing this, write the equation describing the recharging process.

84. Balance the following half reaction.

$$Cr_2O_7^{-2} \rightarrow Cr^{+3}$$

85. Name the following and predict if they are soluble in water.

Na_2S

CrS

$Fe(OH)_2$

BaS

86. Predict the product from the reaction of lithium hydroxide and nitric acid.

87. Predict the product from reaction of chromium II nitrate and sodium sulfide.

88. What ions, if any, are formed when sodium sulfate is added to water?

89. Underline the following that are strong acids.

Nitric acid

Acetic acid

Barium hydroxide

citric acid

H_2SO_4

90. Underline the following that are strong bases.

NaOH

NaCl

KCl

KNO_3

$Ca(OH)_2$

91. Is the following reaction a redox reaction and if so why?

$$2Mg + O_2 \rightarrow 2MgO$$

ANSWERS

1. For the chemical reaction between nitrogen, hydrogen forming ammonium shown below (not balanced) what is the product(s) and what is(are) the reactant(s)?

$$N_2 + H_2 \rightarrow NH_3$$

The reactants are $N_2 + H_2$ and the product is NH_3.

2. What does the $\rightarrow$ mean in chemical reactions?

The $\rightarrow$ is "read" or means "goes to", "forms", "produces", "makes", etc.

3. In a balanced reaction what is balanced?

In a balanced reaction it is the number of each kind of atom that is balanced. This means that on both sides of the equation, product and reactant sides, that the number of each kind of element is the same.

4. What constitutes a balanced equation?

First, that the number of each kind of atom is the same on the product and reactant sides. Second, that the prefixes are whole numbers and the smallest set of whole numbers.

5. Why is $H_2 + O_2 \rightarrow H_2O$ not balanced?

There are two oxygen atoms on the reactant side and only one on the product side.

6. Why is the reaction given below not balanced.

$$H_2 + 1/2\, O_2 \rightarrow H_2O$$

We are to use only whole numbers to balance an equation. 1/2 is not a whole number.

7. Why is the following equation not balanced?

$$4H_2 + 2\,O_2 \rightarrow 4H_2O$$

The set of prefixes 4, 2, and 4 are not the smallest group of whole number.

8. Why it the following equation not balanced?

$$2H_2 + O_2 \rightarrow 2H_2O$$

It is balanced.

9. Balance the chemical reaction

$$N_2 + H_2 \rightarrow NH_3$$

We see that we have two nitrogen atoms on the reactant side and only one on the product side. We multiple the NH_3 by two giving the same number of nitrogen atoms on both sides.

$$N_2 + H_2 \rightarrow 2NH_3$$

We now have 2 hydrogen atoms on the reactant side and 6 hydrogen atoms on the product side. We can multiple H_2 by 3 to get our needed 6 hydrogen atoms giving

$$N_2 + 3H_2 \rightarrow 2NH_3$$

These prefixes are also known as coefficients and they multiple the compound/element after them. So the $2NH_3$ says that we have two molecules/moles of NH_3 and the $3H_2$ signifies that we have three H_2 molecules/moles. There is an understood one in front of the N_2. Thus the coefficient group is often given as 1,3,2 simply being the coefficients in order that they appear in the balanced equation.

10. Write and balance the reaction for the combustion (burning) of octane, C_8H_{18}, in air (reactant is oxygen, O_2).

First, write the equation.

$$C_8H_{18} + O_2 \rightarrow CO_2 + H_2O$$

There are many ways to go but let us notice that we have 8 carbons in octane so multiple CO_2 by eight.

$$C_8H_{18} + O_2 \rightarrow 8CO_2 + H_2O$$

On the reactant side we have now 18 hydrogen atoms associated with the C_8H_{18} so let us multiple the hydrogen-containing product, H_2O by 9 (since there are two hydrogen atoms per water molecule) and we have now

$$C_8H_{18} + O_2 \rightarrow 8CO_2 + 9H_2O$$

At this point we have all of the carbon atoms and hydrogen atoms balanced, but still have oxygen atoms to balance. From the $8CO_2$ we have 16 oxygen atoms and from the $9H_2O$ we have 9 oxygen atoms for a total of $16 + 9 = 25$ oxygen atoms on the product side. This equates to 12.5 oxygen molecules (two oxygen atoms per oxygen molecule). Thus our equation is now

$$C_8H_{18} + 12.5O_2 \rightarrow 8CO_2 + 9H_2O$$

since 1/2 is not a whole number we will simply multiple everything by 2 giving

$$2C_8H_{18} + 25\,O_2 \rightarrow 16\,CO_2 + 18\,H_2O$$

11. Balance the following reaction.

$$HCl + O_2 \rightarrow H_2O + Cl_2$$

We see that there is one oxygen on the reactant side and two on the product since so we will multiple H_2O by two giving

$$HCl + O_2 \rightarrow 2H_2O + Cl_2$$

We next see that the number of hydrogen atoms on the reactant side is only one and on the product side is 4 so we will multiple HCl by 4 giving

$$4HCl + O_2 \rightarrow 2H_2O + Cl_2$$

We also notice that only the number of chlorine atoms are not balanced. We have four chlorine atoms on the reactant side and two on the product side so we will multiple Cl_2 by 2 giving us the needed 4 chlorine atoms and a balanced equation.

$$4HCl + O_2 \rightarrow 2H_2O + 2Cl_2$$

Balancing equations requires work and practice.

12. The reaction between an acid and base forms water and a salt and is exothermic. Write the reaction between sodium hydroxide and hydrochloric acid and show which side of the equation the heat is. Heat is a form of energy and we often use these terms interchangeably though heat is only one form of energy. We can have other forms of energy including magnetic energy.

$$NaOH + HCl \rightarrow NaCl + H_2O + heat \text{ (energy)}$$

13. Write a balanced equation for the reaction between nitrogen and oxygen forming nitrogen monooxide. It is an endothermic equation.

$$N_2 + O_2 + energy \rightarrow 2NO$$

As noted above, heat is a form of energy and they are often used interchangeably.

14. Write the molecular, ionic and net reaction for the reaction between ammonium hydroxide and sulfuric acid. Identify the spectator ions.
    Molecular

$$NH_4OH + H_2SO_4 \rightarrow (NH_4)_2SO_4 + H_2O$$

$$Base + Acid \rightarrow Salt + Water$$

Ionic

$$NH_4OH + 2H^+ + SO_4^{-2} \rightarrow 2NH_4^+ + SO_4^{-2} + H_2O$$

Net Ionic

$$NH_4OH + 2H^+ + SO_4^{-2} \rightarrow 2NH_4^+ + SO_4^{-2} + H_2O$$

Notes- the NH_4OH is a weak base so it does not appreciably ionize in water; that is it does not appreciably form ions in water. Sulfuric acid is a strong acid so it does form lots of ions. The salt, ammonium sulfate, is water soluble and forms ions. Water does not appreciably form ions. There are no spectator ions.

Reactions between acids and bases are called neutralization reactions because the acid and base react with one another neutralizing each another forming water.

15. Write the molecular, ionic and net reaction for the reaction between potassium hydroxide and hydrobromic acid. Identify the spectator ions.
    Molecular

$$KOH + HBr \rightarrow KBr + H_2O$$

$$Base + Acid \rightarrow Salt + Water$$

Ionic

$$K^+ + OH^- + H^+ + Br^- \rightarrow K^+ + Br^- + H_2O$$

Net Ionic

$$OH^- + H^+ \rightarrow H_2O$$

The spectator ions are K^+ and Br^-.

16. Write the molecular, ionic and net reaction for the reaction between iron III nitrate and potassium phosphate. Identify the spectator ions.

Molecular

$$Fe(NO_3)_3 + K_3PO_4 \rightarrow FePO_4 + 3KNO_3$$

Ionic

$$Fe^{+3} + 3NO_3^- + 3K^+ + PO_4^{-3} \rightarrow FePO_4 + 3K^+ + 3NO_3^-$$

Net Ionic

$$Fe^{+3} + 3NO_3^- + 3K^+ + PO_4^{-3} \rightarrow FePO_4 + 3K^+ + 3NO_3^-$$

Notes. Most phosphates are insoluble in water so do not form ions. Most nitrates are soluble in water. The spectator ions are NO_3^- and K^+.

17. Which of the following is **not** a strong acid?

HI   Nitric acid

Sulfuric acid   Acetic acid-a weak acid

18. Which is **not** a strong electrolyte?

AgBr   Insoluble so not a strong electrolyte

NaOH   Strong base so strong electrolyte

$FePO_4$ Not soluble so not a strong electrolyte

NaI   Soluble salt so a strong electrolyte

19. In an aqueous solution of sodium carbonate the addition of which will cause the formation of a precipitate and what is the formula of the precipitate?

$Sr(NO_3)_2$ Formation of insoluble $Sr(CO_3)_2$

NaI   No precipitate formed

Note, an aqueous solution is simply a solution where the solvent is water.

20. What is the oxidation number of chromium in $K_2Cr_2O_7$ and $CrCl_3$?

The oxidation number of chromium in $K_2Cr_2O_7$ is plus 6. Remember that oxidation numbers are figured for a single atom. The oxidation number of chromium in $CrCl_3$ is +3.

21. What is the oxidation number of tin in $SnCl_2$ and $SnCl_4$?

The oxidation number for tin in $SnCl_2$ is a + 2 and for tin in $SnCl_4$ it is +4.

22. What is oxidized and reduced, losing and gaining electrons, and reducing agent and oxidizing agent in the following equation.

$$K_2Cr_2O_7 + SnCl_2 + HCl \rightarrow CrCl_3 + SnCl_4 + H_2O + KCl$$

Using the calculations made in question 20 we have chromium decreasing from +6 to +3 which is reduction so $K_2Cr_2O_7$ is reduced; it is gaining electrons; and since it is reduced it is an oxidizing agent. From the calculations made in question 21 the tin is gaining in oxidation from a + 2 to a + 4 so $SnCl_2$ is reduced and is losing electrons and since it is oxidized, it is a reducing agent.

Remember, that answers to who is oxidized, reduced, losing electrons, gaining electrons, oxidizing agents, and reducing agent always appear on the reactant side, never on the product side.

23. What is the oxidation number of iron in FeS and in $FeCl_3$?
    In FeS the oxidation number of iron is +2 and in $FeCl_3$ it is +3.

24. What is the oxidation number of nitrogen in HNO_3 and NO?
    In HNO_3 it is +5 and in NO it is +2.

25. In the following reaction which is oxidized, reduced, losing and gaining electrons, and an oxidizing and reducing agent?

$$FeS + KCl + HNO_3 \rightarrow NO + K_2SO_4 + FeCl_3 + H_2O$$

Using the calculations made in question 23 we see that iron has gone from a + 2 on the product side to a + 3 on the product side. Thus, it has gained in oxidation number so FeS is oxidized, lost electrons and is a reducing agent. Using the calculations we made in question 24 nitrogen has lost oxidation number from +5 on the reactant side of the equation in HNO_3 to +2 in NO so HNO_3 has been reduced, gained electrons and is an oxidizing agent.

26. To balance the combustion of methane, CH_4, what should be placed in front of the oxygen molecule.

The products of combustion are carbon dioxide and water.

$$CH_4 + O_2 \rightarrow CO_2 + H_2O$$

The balanced equation is

$$CH_4 + 2O_2 \rightarrow CO_2 + 2H_2O$$

so a "2" is placed before the oxygen molecule.

27. What is the oxidation numbers of all of the elements in potassium phosphate?

The formula for potassium phosphate is K_3PO_4. We know that the oxidation number for K in a compound is +1 and we have 3 of them for a total of +3; the oxidation number for oxygen is usually −2 in compounds and we have 4 of them for a total of −8. Since the compound is neutral, the oxidation number for P is $+3 − 8 = +5$.

28. What is the oxidation number for Fe in $FeBr_2$? We have that halides, of which Br is one, typically have an oxidation number of −1 in compounds. Since there are two Br's we have a net −2 due to the bromides. Since the compound is neutral iron must have an oxidation number of +2. We actually used this in our naming of such compounds. Thus, $FeBr_2$ is iron II bromide where the II is the oxidation number of iron in $FeBr_2$.

29. Make bold only those compounds that are strong electrolytes.

$PbSO_4$ not soluble thus does not form ions

HNO_3   strong acid thus forms lots of ions-a strong acid and strong electrolyte.

KOH   strong base thus forms lots of ions-a strong base and strong electrolyte

30. Make bold only those compounds that are strong electrolytes.

Sugar   soluble in water but does not form ions

NH_4OH weak base so forms only a few ions; weak electrolyte

Citric Acid   weak acid so forms only a few ions; weak electrolyte

31. What is the oxidation number of each element in the following?

CuCl   Cl −1; Thus Cu is +1

NaOH   Na +1, H +1, O −2

H_2S H +1; S −2

32. A leprechaun is suspected of being a terrorist and hording precious metals. The CIA break into his home and in the basement finds two 55 gallon drums. The labels are found on the ground- potassium nitrate and silver nitrate. Using simple chemicals found in the home, how can the agents differentiate between the contents of the two drums? Is the evidence consistent with the leprechaun possibly being a terrorist and hording precious metals?

Can use water from the faucet and table salt which is NaCl. Dissolve the table salt in two separate glasses of water. Dissolve in separate glasses the silver nitrate and potassium nitrate. Add some of the dissolved material from one of the 55 gallon drums to one of the glasses containing the dissolved NaCl. If a precipitate forms then that drum contains the silver nitrate since it has formed AgCl which is insoluble in water. If no precipitate forms then that drum contains potassium nitrate since potassium chloride is water soluble.

Now the question of what the leprechaun is, is not easy to answer since he may want to hoard the silver in the silver nitrate and use the potassium nitrate to fertilize his yard- or indeed he may be a terrorist. Only the leprechaun truly knows.

33. Which of the following is a **strong** acid?

KOH   strong base

LiOH   strong base

HBr   **strong acid**

34. Which of the following is a strong base **OR** strong acid?

$Ca(OH)_2$ **strong base**

Phosphoric acid   weak acid

Acetic acid   weak acid

35. Which of the following are water soluble?

Sodium phosphate   Most phosphates are not water soluble but group I are so this is soluble

Silver phosphate   Most phosphates are not water soluble and this is no exception

Disulfur trioxide   Not included in our solubility table.

36. Which of the following are water soluble?

Aluminum acetate   Acetates are generally soluble and this is an acetate so soluble

| Titanium nitrate | Nitrates are soluble so this is soluble |
| Platinum sulfate | Most sulfates are soluble and this is not one of the exceptions |

37. Which of the following are water soluble?

Barium sulfate	Most sulfates are soluble but this is an exception since it is paired with barium so it is not soluble
$V(NO_3)_2$	Most nitrates are soluble and this is probably soluble
$CrSO_4$	Most sulfates are soluble and this is not one of the exceptions so it is soluble

38. Which of the following are water soluble?

BaS	Most sulfides are not soluble and this is not an exception so it is not soluble
$FeSO_4$	Most sulfates are soluble and this is not an exception so it is soluble
$CaCO_3$	Most carbonates are not soluble and this is not an exception fortunately for those in south Florida since this is limestone

39. To balance the following simple redox half cell how many electrons must be added/taken away?

$$Na \rightarrow Na^+$$

Note that the changes on both sides of the equation must be the same. We can do this by adding an electron, e^-, on the product side so that a single electron is taken from the sodium.

$$Na \rightarrow Na^+ + e^-$$

40. In problem 39 is this an oxidation or reduction half cell?

Sodium increases its oxidation number from zero to one so it is an oxidation half cell.

41. To balance the following redox half cell how many electrons must be added/taken away? Is this an oxidation or reduction half cell?

$$2Cl^- \rightarrow Cl_2$$

The charges on both sides of the equation must be the same. To do this we can add two electrons to the product side as follows so two electrons are then taken from

$2Cl^-$. The oxidation number increases from -1 for Cl^- to zero for each chlorine atom in the chlorine molecule so it is an oxidation half cell.

$$2Cl^- \rightarrow Cl_2 + 2e^-$$

42. For the half cell

$$MnO_4^- \rightarrow MnO$$

how many water molecules must be added / taken away in the balanced half cell occurring under acidic (acid) conditions.

First, let us note the oxidation change. The oxidation number of Mn in MnO_4^- is +7 and in MnO it is +2 so 5 electrons are exchanged. This half cell is a reduction half cell since the oxidation number for Mn is decreased from 7 to 2. In reduction, electrons are gained on the reactant side giving

$$5e^- + MnO_4^- \rightarrow MnO$$

Next we note that the number of oxygen atoms on both sides of the half cell are not the same. In acidic (acid) reactions we use H^+ and H_2O to adjust the number of oxygen and hydrogen atoms. First, let us add three water molecules to the right side so we now have four oxygen atoms on each side of the equation.

$$5e^- + MnO_4^- \rightarrow MnO + 3H_2O$$

but we have created another imbalance of atoms, here hydrogen atoms so that the product side has 6 hydrogen atoms and the reactant side has no hydrogen atoms. So we add $6H^+$ to the reactant side giving

$$5e^- + 6H^+ + MnO_4^- \rightarrow MnO + 3H_2O$$

We now have a balanced half cell. Note, again the total change on both sides of the equation is the same, here zero.

43. What is the hallmark of a strong acid?
Forms lots of protons in comparison to the number of proton-containing units added. Thus for each HCl added to water, one proton and one chloride ion is formed.

44. What is the hallmark of a strong electrolyte?
Forms lots of ions in comparison to the number of units added. Thus, for the strong electrolyte potassium chloride for every potassium chloride added, one potassium ion and one chloride ion are formed in water.

45. Which of the following forms the largest number of ions from addition of one mole to ten liters of water?
Na_3PO_4 This forms the most- $Na_3PO_4 \rightarrow 3Na^+ + PO_4^{-3}$
NaOH
AgI
$CaCl_2$

46. For the below potential energy profile identify what the products and reactants are.

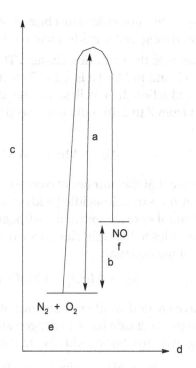

The products are NO, f; and the reactants are N_2 and O_2, e.

47. For the potential energy profile given in problem 46 what is a?

"a" is the activation energy or energy of activation.

48. For the potential energy profile given in problem 46 what is b?

"b" is the heat of reaction.

49. For the reaction potential energy profile given in problem 46 is the reaction exothermic or endothermic? Why?

The reaction is endothermic because the potential energy level for the products is higher or less than the potential energy level for the reactants; thus the products possess less potential energy in comparison to the reactants and this difference is given off in terms of energy, usually heat energy.

50. Write the balanced equation for the reaction described in problem 46 including which side the net heat will occur.

$$N_2 + O_2 \rightarrow 2NO + heat$$

51. If you are holding onto a beaker that has a highly endothermic reaction occurring in it, what evidence will you have that the reaction is endothermic?

The beaker will feel cool since energy is being taken from the environment and your hand is part of the environment that is supplying the energy.

52. Which of the following is a strong base? NaOH, LiOH, $Ca(OH)_2$, HCl, $CaCl_2$.

NaOH, LiOH, and $Ca(OH)_2$ are strong bases.

53. What is the connection between strong acids and bases and strong electrolytes?

Both strong acids, bases, and strong electrolytes are essentially 100% ionized.

54. $BaSO_4$ is ionic and yet it is not an electrolyte. Why?

$BaSO_4$ is not soluble in water so it does not form ions and thus is not an electrolyte.

55. Write the ionic equation for Na_3PO_4 in water.

$$Na_3PO_4 \rightarrow 3\,Na^+ + PO_4^{-3}$$

56. Which of the following are not soluble in water? KOH, K_2S, PbS, $(NH_4)_3PO_4$, $Ti(CO_3)_2$.

All but $Ti(CO_3)_2$ are soluble in water.

57. Why does the solubility of most compounds increase when heated?

Increased temperature helps ions to overcome attractive forces allowing greater solubility.

58. If you have a solution of $NaNO_3$ which of the following soluble chlorides will form a precipitate when added to the solution. Ca^{+2}, Ni^{+2}, Fe^{+2}, Co^{+2}.

Essentially all "usual" cation salts are soluble in nitrate solutions.

59. When solutions of silver nitrate and potassium iodide are brought together a _____ reaction occurs forming _____ as a solid.

$$AgNO_3 + KI \rightarrow AgI \text{ (precipitate)} + KNO_3$$

AgI is formed in a precipitation reaction.

60. Which of the following will produce the greatest amount of ions? $Ca_3(PO_4)_2$, NaCl, $BaCl_2$, $Al(NO_3)_3$.

$Ca_3(PO_4)_2$ would except it is not soluble. $Al(NO_3)_3$ gives 4 moles of ions for every mole of $Al(NO_3)_3$ so it forms the greatest number ions per mole of solid added to water.

61. Write the reaction for vanadium V oxide reacting with hydrogen forming vanadium III oxide and water.

$$V_2O_5 + H_2 \rightarrow V_2O_3 + H_2O$$

Balanced it is

$$V_2O_5 + 2H_2 \rightarrow V_2O_3 + 2H_2O$$

62. What is undergoing oxidation in the reaction described in question 61? What is undergoing reduction?

H_2 is undergoing oxidation. V_2O_5 is undergoing reduction.

63. In problem 61 what is gaining electrons? What is the oxidizing agent?

V_2O_5 is gaining electrons and it is the oxidizing agent.

64. The reaction described in problem 61 is a(n) _____ reaction.

Redox or oxidation/reduction reaction.

65. Write the molecular, ionic and net ionic reaction that occurs between HCl and $Pb(NO_3)_2$

Molecular

$$2HI + Pb(NO_3)_2 \rightarrow PbI_2 + 2HNO_3$$

Ionic

$$2H^+ + 2I^- + Pb^{+2} + 2NO_3^- \rightarrow PbI_2 + 2H^+ + 2NO_3^-$$

Net Ionic

$$2I^- + Pb^{+2} + \rightarrow PbI_2$$

66. Write the molecular, ionic and net ionic reaction that occurs between NaBr and $LiNO_3$.

Molecular

$$NaBr + LiNO_3 \rightarrow NaNO_3 + LiBr$$

Ionic

$$Na^+ + Br^- + Li^+ + NO_3^- \rightarrow Na^+ + NO_3^- + Li^+ + Br^-$$

Net Ionic

All the ions cancel so there is no net reaction just a solution containing the soluble ions from the two soluble salts.

67. We generally write the reaction that occurs between hydrogen and oxygen forming water. But in a process called electrolysis we break up water forming hydrogen and oxygen. Write both reactions clearly showing the products from having them on the pointed side of the arrow.

$$2H_2 + O_2 \rightarrow 2H_2O \text{ (product)}$$

$$2H_2O \rightarrow 2H_2 + O_2 \text{ (hydrolysis)}$$

Thus, this reaction is reversible going in both directions depending on the reaction conditions. But, under normal conditions without the external addition of energy, the first reaction overwhelmingly occurs.

68. Give three examples of salts that are soluble in water.

NaCl, KI, $BaBr_2$, etc. Be sure to memorize the solubility table; and KNOW how to use it.

69. The formation of water from hydrogen and oxygen and the combustion of hydrocarbons forming carbon dioxide and water are examples of _____ reactions.

Redox or oxidation/ reduction reactions and/or exothermic reactions.

70. Balance the combustion reaction between ethane, C_2H_6, and oxygen.

First write out the basic reaction.

$$C_2H_6 + O_2 \rightarrow CO_2 + H_2O$$

The balanced equation is as follows. First, since we have two carbons in ethane we will multiple carbon dioxide by 2

$$C_2H_6 + O_2 \rightarrow 2CO_2 + H_2O$$

Next, we will balance our hydrogen atoms by multiplying water by 3.

$$C_2H_6 + O_2 \rightarrow 2CO_2 + 3H_2O$$

we now have 9 hydrogen atoms on the product side and will multiple molecular oxygen by 4.5 to give us the 9 hydrogen atoms.

$$C_2H_6 + 4.5O_2 \rightarrow 2CO_2 + 3H_2O$$

We must have small whole numbers so we will multiple everything by 2 to finally get our balanced equation.

$$2C_2H_6 + 7O_2 \rightarrow 4\,CO_2 + 6\,H_2O$$

71. What is the hallmark of a **weak** base?

A base is a compound that when added to water increases the hydroxide concentration according to the Arrhenius definition. Thus, a weak base will produce relatively a small number of hydroxides in comparison to the number of hydroxyl-containing units added to the water.

72. To recover iron from its oxides carbon is used. The equation for the recovery from iron III oxide is below.

$$Fe_2O_3 + C \rightarrow Fe + CO$$

What is the oxidation numbers for carbon in C and in CO?
For mono-elemental, meaning just one element, materials with no given oxidation number the oxidation number is agreed to be zero. For CO, the oxidation number of oxygen is -2 so the carbon is $+2$. We will also begin to be aware of atoms that are generally involved in changes in oxidation number. Primary candidates are the transition metals, sulfur, carbon, and nitrogen and any atom that changes from being in the zero oxidation state to forming a compound. Fe is a transition element.

73. In 72 what is oxidized and what is reduced?

From problem 72 we see that the oxidation number of carbon increases from zero to $+2$ so C has an increase in oxidation number and is oxidized. The oxidation number of iron in Fe_2O_3 is $+3$ and as a lone standing iron, Fe, it is zero. Thus, the change in the oxidation number of iron is from a $+3$ to 0 so it is a loss in oxidation number. Thus, Fe_2O_3 is reduced.

74. Copper metal is dissolved in the presence of nitric acid according to the following reaction.

$$Cu + NO_3^- \rightarrow Cu^{+2} + NO_2$$

What is oxidized and what is reduced in this process?
Copper metal goes from an oxidation number of zero to $+2$ so its oxidation number increases so Cu is oxidized. Nitrogen's oxidation number goes from a $+5$ in NO_3^- to $+4$ in NO_2 so NO_3^- is reduced.

75. Write the balanced oxidation half-cell for problem 74.

$$Cu \rightarrow Cu^{+2}$$

There is an exchange of one electron for each change in one oxidation number so in going from 0 to +2 there are two electrons involved. The electrons are lost since this is the oxidation half-cell so the two electrons will appear on the product side.

$$Cu \rightarrow Cu^{+2} + 2e^-$$

Notice that the changes on the product and reactant side are the same. The net charge on both sides is zero. They do not need to be zero but do need to be the same.

76. Write the balanced reduction half-cell for problem 74.

$$NO_3^- \rightarrow NO_2$$

Again, there is one electron change for each change in oxidation number. Here, nitrogen goes from a + 5 to a + 4 so there is one electron change. Since this describes reduction the electron is added to the reactant side.

$$NO_3^- + e^- \rightarrow NO_2$$

Now we need to correct for the imbalance in the oxygen atoms. In cases where the reaction is run in water we generally employ the possible components of water, H_2O, H^+ and OH^-. When the reaction is run in acid we use H_2O and H^+. Since we need the addition of one oxygen atom to the product side we add one H_2O to the product side. [As a general practice we add one H_2O for each oxygen atom needed.]

$$NO_3^- + e^- \rightarrow NO_2 + H_2O$$

While we now have the oxygen atoms balanced we have created another imbalance, here in hydrogen atoms. Generally, we simply add any needed hydrogen atoms as H^+ to the side that needs the hydrogen atoms. In this case we need two hydrogen atoms on the reactant side giving

$$NO_3^- + 2H^+ + e^- \rightarrow NO_2 + H_2O$$

We finally have our balanced reduction half-cell. Note that the charges on both sides are now the same.

77. Using the half-cells derived in problems 75 and 76 balance the equation given in problem 74.

We have two balanced half cells-the oxidation half-cell

$$Cu \rightarrow Cu^{+2} + 2e^-$$

and the balanced reduction half-cell:

$$NO_3^- + 2H^+ + e^- \rightarrow NO_2 + H_2O$$

We now add the two half cells. But before we do, we need to remember that the number of electrons added must be the same number of electrons that are taken away; that is, the number of electrons exchanged must be the same. Two electrons are present in the oxidation half-cell and one is present in the reduction half-cell. Thus, we can simply multiply the reduction half-cell by two giving

$$2NO_3^- + 4H^+ + 2e^- \rightarrow 2NO_2 + 2H_2O$$

We now add the two half cells giving

$$2NO_3^- + 4H^+ + 2e^- + Cu \rightarrow 2NO_2 + 2H_2O + Cu^{+2} + 2e^-$$

We now eliminate the items that are the same on both sides of the equation, here only the electrons, giving us the balanced equation.

$$2NO_3^- + 4H^+ + Cu \rightarrow 2NO_2 + 2H_2O + Cu^{+2}$$

78. The reaction between tin +2 and the permanganate ion is described as follows.

$$Sn^{+2} + MnO_4^- \rightarrow Sn^{+4} + Mn^{+2}$$

What is oxidized and what is reduced?

Tin changes from a + 2 to a + 4 for an increase in oxidation number so tin is oxidized. Mn changes from a + 7 to a + 2 for a decrease in oxidation number so MnO_4^- is reduced. In fact, you will begin to recognize compounds that are typically oxidizing agents- here it is the permanganate ion.

79. Write the balanced reduction half-cell for the equation given in problem 78.

$$MnO_4^- \rightarrow Mn^{+2}$$

The oxidation number changes from a + 7 to +2 for an oxidation number change of 5 units corresponding to an exchange of 5 electrons. Since this is the reduction half-cell, electrons are gained so they will appear on the reactant side of the equation.

$$5e^- + MnO_4^- \rightarrow Mn^{+2}$$

Next we correct for the number of oxygen atoms by adding four water molecules to the product side.

$$5e^- + MnO_4^- \rightarrow Mn^{+2} + 4H_2O$$

And, finally addition of the necessary protons to the reactant side.

$$5e^- + 8H^+ + MnO_4^- \rightarrow Mn^{+2} + 4H_2O$$

Again, note that the change on both side is the same, here +2.

80. Write the balanced oxidation half-cell for the equation given in problem 78.

$$Sn^{+2} \rightarrow Sn^{+4}$$

The number of electrons changed is two and since this is the oxidation half-cell, the electrons will appear on the product side, that is, electrons are lost.

$$Sn^{+2} \rightarrow Sn^{+4} + 2e^-$$

81. Balance the equation given in problem 78.

Again, we will eventually simply add the reduction and oxidation half-cell but first we need to have the number of electrons being lost and gained, exchanged, the same. The number of electrons being exchanged in oxidation is two and in reduction it is five. We can get the same number by multiplying the oxidation half-cell by 5 and the reduction half-cell by 2 giving the following.

$$5Sn^{+2} \rightarrow 5Sn^{+4} + 10e^-$$

$$10e^- + 16H^+ + 2MnO_4^- \rightarrow 2Mn^{+2} + 8H_2O$$

Addition and elimination of the protons gives:

$$16H^+ + 2MnO_4^- + 5Sn^{+2} \rightarrow 2Mn^{+2} + 8H_2O + Sn^{+4}$$

82. Our automobiles often require a battery to start the engine. The most common battery is called the lead storage battery. The energy to start the engine is supplied by the exchange of electrons in the battery. The balanced redox reaction is described as follows.

$$Pb + PbO_2 + 2H_2SO_4 \rightarrow 2PbSO_4 + 2H_2O$$

What is oxidized and what is reduced?

This is one of a few redox reactions where the product of both reduction and oxidation is the same, in this case $PbSO_4$. Pb in Pb goes from an oxidation number of zero to +2 in $PbSO_4$ so this is oxidation since the oxidation number increases. And Pb in PbO_2 goes from an oxidation number of +4 to +2 in $PbSO_4$ so this is reduction since the oxidation decreases.

83. The reaction described in problem 82 occurs in sulfuric acid which is called the battery acid. Sulfuric acid is a <u>strong</u>/weak electrolyte and a <u>strong</u>/weak acid. Underline the correct term.

In automobiles, the alternator allows the battery to be recharged so that the battery life is extended from a few starts to thousands of starts. The equation describing the recharging is simply the reverse reaction. Knowing this, write the equation describing the recharging process.

$$2PbSO_4 + 2H_2O \rightarrow Pb + PbO_2 + 2H_2SO_4$$

84. Balance the following half reaction.

$$Cr_2O_7^{-2} \rightarrow Cr^{+3}$$

The oxidation number for Cr in $Cr_2O_7^{-2}$ is +6 for each single Cr atom. The oxidation number of Cr^{+3} is +3 as given. The change in oxidation number is from a +6 to a +3 , oxidation, or a change of 3 oxidation units corresponding to 3 electrons change. Since it is a reduction the electrons will appear as electrons added to the reactant side. Let us remember that the balance with respect to Cr atoms is actually

$$Cr_2O_7^{-2} \rightarrow 2Cr^{+3}$$

so that the number of electrons added is 2×3 or six.

$$Cr_2O_7^{-2} + 6e^- \rightarrow 2Cr^{+3}$$

Next let us correct for the oxygen atom imbalance by adding seven water molecules to the product side and finally 14 protons to the reactant side giving

$$Cr_2O_7^{-2} + 6e^- + 14H^+ \rightarrow 2Cr^{+3} + 7H_2O$$

and the net charges on each side of the arrow being +6.

85. Name the following and predict if they are soluble in water.

Na_2S	Sodium sulfide	Soluble
CrS	Chromium II sulfide	Insoluble
$Fe(OH)_2$	Iron II hydroxide	Insoluble
BaS	Barium sulfide	Soluble

86. Predict the product from the reaction of lithium hydroxide and nitric acid.

    The reaction is a simple neutralization reaction.

    $$HNO_3 + LiOH \rightarrow LiNO_3 + H_2O$$

    The general scheme for such simple acid-base reactions is

    Acid + Base $\rightarrow$ Salt + Water.

87. Predict the product from reaction of chromium II nitrate and sodium sulfide.

    $$Cr(NO_3)_2 + Na_2S \rightarrow CrS_{(s)} + 2NaNO_3$$

    The CuS is not water soluble so it precipitates from solution. The general type reaction is a precipitation reaction.

88. What ions, if any, are formed when sodium sulfate is added to water?

    Sodium sulfate is water soluble so sodium ions and sulfate ions are formed as follows:

    $$Na_2SO_4 \rightarrow 2Na^+ + SO_4^{-2}$$

89. Underline the following that are strong acids.

    <u>Nitric acid</u>

    Acetic acid

    Barium hydroxide

    citric acid

    <u>H_2SO_4</u>

90. Underline the following that are strong bases.

    <u>NaOH</u>

    NaCl

    KCl

    KNO_3

    <u>$Ca(OH)_2$</u>

91. Is the following reaction a redox reaction and if so why?

    $$2Mg + O_2 \rightarrow 2MgO$$

    It is a redox reaction because the oxidation numbers for Mg and oxygen change from the reactant side to the product side.

SAMPLE TEST PROBLEMS

Name _____ Date _____

Circle only correct answers.

92. What are the spectator ions for the reaction of silver nitrate and sodium chloride in water?
a. Na^+, H_2O; b. $AgCl$; c. $AgNO_3$; d. Na^+, NO_3^-; e. Na^+, Cl^-

93. What is the salt formed from the reaction of lithium hydroxide and sulfuric acid?
a. Li_2SO_4; b. $LiSO_4$; c. H_2O; d. $LiOH$; e. $Li(SO_4)_2$

94. Which of the following is soluble in water?
a. $BaSO_4$; b. $FeSO_4$; c. $FePO_4$; d. $CaCO_3$; e. CrS

95. What must be in front of O_2 in the combustion of methane, CH_4, forming carbon dioxide and water in a balanced equation?
a. 1; b. 2; c. 3; d. 4; e. 6

96. Which of the following is a strong base?
a. $AlCl_3$; b. $Al(OH)_3$; c. CH_3OH; d. HNO_3; e. $LiOH$

97. Which of the following forms the most ions per mole when added to water?
a. Na_3PO_4; b. $AgCl$; c. $NaCl$; d. $BaSO_4$; e. $NaOH$

98. What is the oxidation number of iron in $FePO_4$?
a. +3; b. −2; c. −3; d. +2; e. +1

99. In the following reaction what is reduced?

$$V_2O_5 + H_2 \rightarrow V_2O_3 + H_2O$$

a. V_2O_5; b. H_2; c. V_2O_3; d. H_2O e. V

100. For the half-cell

$$NO_3^- \rightarrow NO_2$$

how many electrons are being added/lost?
a. 1 electron lost; b. 1 electron gained; c. 2 electrons lost;
d. 2 electrons gained; e. 3 electrons added

101. What kind of reaction is

$$Pb(NO_3)_2 + Na_2SO_4 \rightarrow$$

a. Redox; b. Oxidation; c. Precipitation; d. Reduction;
e. Neutralization

Reaction Stoichiometry

IMPORTANCE OF A BALANCED EQUATION

Why is a balanced equation important? They are important since the coefficients tell us how many moles/molecules of each are involved in the balanced reaction. Thus, for

$$H_2 + N_2 \rightarrow NH_3$$

We notice that this is not balanced. To balance we will multiple the H_2 by 3 and the NH_3 by two giving

$$3H_2 + N_2 \rightarrow 2NH_3$$

This means that 3 molecules of hydrogen reacts with one molecule of nitrogen producing two molecules of ammonia; that 3 moles of hydrogen reacts with one mole of nitrogen producing two moles of ammonia; and that 6 molecules of hydrogen reacts with two molecule of nitrogen producing 4 molecules of ammonia; and that 9 moles of hydrogen reacts with 3 mole of nitrogen producing 6 moles of ammonia; etc.

The counting factors relating the reactants and products are **moles** and **molecules**. And, the **coefficients** give the **ratio** of **products** and **reactants**-for this reaction the ratio is 3 to 1 to 2.

To work many problems that require several steps to solve we need to develop a strategy often taking the form of a "road map"-like description that directs us from the start of the problem to the final answer. These are also referred to as **strategy directions/maps**, **road-maps** or **solution maps**. We will use all of these terms during our discussions as to how to work multistep problems. For so-called weight-weight problems the road map might look like the following.

Solution Map
Weight → Moles → Balanced Equation → Moles → Weight

This is a **reversible** road map-that is we can go in either direction.

Balanced reactions form much of the basis for determining the quantitative relationships in chemical reactions. Thus, for the reaction of

$$2H_2 + O_2 \rightarrow 2H_2O$$

we know the relationships between all of the reactants. Thus, we know that
2 moles of hydrogen react with one mole of oxygen giving 2 moles of water

30 molecules	react with 15 molecules	giving 30 molecules
2.6 moles	react with 1.3 moles	giving 2.6 moles

always using the **precise ratio** of the **coefficients** of the **balanced** equation

but **NOT**

3 GRAMS   REACT WITH 1.5 GRAMS   GIVING 3 GRAMS

in other words-the ratio of reactants and products is

$$2 \text{ to } 1 \rightarrow 2$$

using as the "counting factor" the **coefficients** of the **balanced equation**.

We are able to associate masses through remembering that

one **mole = one gram formula weight or one molecular weight.**

There are different approaches to telling how many molecules or moles is needed using a balanced equation given the moles of one reactant. Following is one called the proportion approach.

How many moles of water can be made from 5 moles of oxygen, O_2?

This type of problem is referred to as a **mole-mole problem** since we are given the number of moles of one material and asked to determine the number of moles of a second material.

We have the balanced relationship between hydrogen, oxygen and water as follows:

$$2H_2 + O_2 \rightarrow 2\,H_2O$$

The mole relationship between oxygen and water in the **balanced** equation is $1 O_2 \longrightarrow 2\,H_2O$. We than can set up the proportion as follows

$$\frac{1O_2}{5} = \frac{2H_2O}{X} \qquad \text{And solving for X = 10.}$$

How many moles of hydrogen are needed to produce 5 moles of ammonia according to the balanced equation given below describing the production of ammonia using the Haber process?

For the Haber process used to produce ammonia the balanced equation is

$$N_2 + 3H_2 \rightarrow 2NH_3$$

Again, set up the proportion $\dfrac{3H_2}{X} = \dfrac{2NH_3}{5}$

Solving for X = 15/2 = 7.5 moles of hydrogen are needed.

What weight of nitrogen, N_2, is required to produce 68 grams of ammonia, NH_3?

This kind of problem is referred to as a **weight-weight problem** since we are given a weight of one material and asked to determine the weight of a second material.

First we create a solution map as follows:

Weight ammonia → moles of ammonia → balanced equation → moles nitrogen → weight nitrogen

In this solution map we neglected two additional chores that must be done. Both of these chores are to determine the formula weight of the each of the materials- the given material, here ammonia, and the ending material, here nitrogen. For every problem requiring us to convert a weight of a material into moles we are required to do this unless the formula weight is given in the problem.

Further, unless otherwise noted, we will assume that the other materials are present in excess so that we can focus on only the materials given in the problem.

First step → weight ammonia → moles of ammonia

To accomplish this we determine the gram formula weight of ammonia as follows:

$1N \times 14\,amu/N = 14\,amu$

$3H \times 1\,amu/H = 3\,amu$

$GFW = 17\,amu$ or 17 grams/mole

You recall that Gram Formula Weight, GFW or gfw = Gram Molecular Weight, GMW or gmw because ammonia is covalently bonded

Number of moles = given weight/gfw = 68 grams/17 grams/mole = 4 moles

Next step

moles ammonia → balanced equation → moles nitrogen

For this step we will use a proportion approach. We set up the proportion using the coefficients for the balanced equation as follows

$$\frac{1\,N_2}{X \text{ moles } N_2} = \frac{2NH_3}{4 \text{ moles } NH_3}$$

Solving for X using cross multiplication gives $2X = 4$ and $X = 4/2 = 2$ moles of N_2 that can be made from 68 grams of ammonia.

How many grams of ammonia are produced from 12 moles of nitrogen using the Haber process?

The proportion is then

$$\frac{1N_2}{12} = \frac{2NH_3}{X}$$

and X = 24 moles of ammonia

Grams of ammonia = number of moles of ammonia times gram formula weight of ammonia = 24 moles × 17 grams/mole = 408 grams

This is referred to as the **theoretical** or **maximum yield** since it is the most product that can be produced.

How many moles of ammonia can be produced from 36 grams of hydrogen and 168 grams of nitrogen using the Haber process?

This problem is referred to as a **limiting agent** or **limiting reagent problem** because we are given the weights of two materials and asked to calculate the maximum amount of a third material needed to react with these two materials. The chemical agent that gives us the least amount of the third material is called the limiting reagent or limiting agent.

To do this type of problem requires us to do two weight-weight problems and then comparing the weights to determine the maximum amount of material that can be produced-the smaller amount produced.

First, let us determine the amount of ammonia that can be produced from 36 grams of hydrogen.

weight hydrogen → moles hydrogen → balanced equation → moles ammonia → weight ammonia

moles H_2 = wt H_2/gfw H_2 = 36 grams H_2/ 2 grams./mole = 18 moles H_2

$$\frac{3\,H_2}{18 \text{ moles } H_2} = \frac{2\,NH_3}{X \text{ moles } NH_3}$$

$3X = 2 \times 18 = 36$ and $X = 36/3 = 12$ moles NH_3

Weight = moles NH_3 times gfw NH_3 = 12 moles $NH_3 \times 17$ g/mole = 204 grams NH_3

We will now do a similar problem except to determine the amount of NH_3 produced from 168 grams of N_2.

weight nitrogen → moles nitrogen → balanced equation → moles NH_3 → weight NH_3

moles N_2 = 168 g/28 grams/mole = 8 moles N_2

$$\frac{1\ N_2}{8\ \text{moles}\ N_2} = \frac{2\ NH_3}{X\ \text{moles}\ NH_3}$$

$X = 2 \times 8 = 16$ moles NH_3

Weight = moles NH_3 times gfw NH_3 = 16 moles $NH_3 \times 17$ g/mole = 272 grams NH_3

We next compare the weight from 36 grams of hydrogen, 204 grams of NH_3 to the weight from 168 grams of nitrogen, 272 grams NH_3 and see which is smaller. Obviously 204 is a smaller number than 272 so the maximum amount we can make is 204 grams and hydrogen is the limiting agent.

This proportion approach is also good for solving other kinds of problems.

If 4 grams of a compound contains 1.8×10^{23} repeat units, then one mole weights how many grams.

$$\frac{4\ \text{grams}}{X\ \text{grams}} = \frac{1.8 \times 10^{23}}{6 \times 10^{23}} \quad \text{And}\ X = 13.3\ \text{grams}$$

How many moles of iron atoms are in 6.00 grams of iron? You could remember that the number of moles = weight / g formula weight or

$$\frac{6\ \text{grams}}{56\ \text{grams}} = \frac{X\ \text{moles}}{1\ \text{mole}} \quad \text{And}\ X = 0.107\ \text{moles}$$

We will illustrate additional problems that can be solved using this proportion approach later.

There are several approaches to solving this type of problem. Another approach is to string together the problem working again on a similar problem solving strategy, road map. We will solve two problems using this approach. The approaches are similar except in this approach the steps are strung together.

Thus, calculate the weight of carbon dioxide formed from the combustion of 500 grams or 5×10^2 grams of octane. For brevity we have that the molecular weight for octane is 114 g/mole and for carbon dioxide it is 44 g/mole.

Our strategy map is

grams octane → moles octane → moles carbon dioxide → weight of carbon dioxide

We begin with a balanced equation.

$$2C_8H_{18} + 25\ O_2 \rightarrow 16\ CO_2 + 18\ H_2O$$

$$5.0 \times 10^2\ \text{g}\ C_8H_{18} \times \frac{1 \text{mol}\ C_8H_{18}}{114\ \text{g}\ C_8H_{18}} \times \frac{16\ \text{mol}\ CO_2}{2\ \text{mol}\ C_8H_{18}} \times \frac{44\ \text{g}\ CO_2}{1\ \text{mol}\ CO_2} = 1.5 \times 10^3\ \text{g}\ CO_2$$

You will notice that the coefficients for the balanced equation are present in the third term.

Let us work a second problem using this approach. How many grams of glucose, $C_6H_{12}O_6$, can be produced from 58.5 grams of CO_2 using the following balanced equation?

$$6CO_2 + 6H_2O \rightarrow 6O_2 + C_6H_{12}O_6$$

Again, to assist us the molecular weight of CO_2 is 44 grams/mole and for $C_6H_{12}O_6$ it is 180 grams/mole.

Our strategy map for this problem is

grams of $CO_2 \rightarrow$ moles $CO_2 \rightarrow$ moles $C_6H_{12}O_6 \rightarrow$ grams $C_6H_{12}O_6$

$$58.5 \text{ g } CO_2 \times \frac{1 \text{ mol } CO_2}{44 \text{ g } CO_2} \times \frac{1 \text{ mol } C_6H_{12}O_6}{6 \text{ mol } CO_2} \times \frac{180 \text{ g } C_6H_{12}O_6}{1 \text{ mol } C_6H_{12}O_6} = 40 \text{ g } C_6H_{12}O_6$$

Again, you will notice that the coefficients for the balanced equation are present in the third term.

You will note that this reaction is the reverse of the combustion of octane or any other hydrocarbon. Second, this reaction describes the synthesis, by photosynthesis, of $C_6H_{12}O_6$, glucose.

You can use either approach or some other approach to solve this type of problem but make sure your approach works and that you understand what you are doing.

We will practice the proportion method as follows.

The Haber process for the synthesis of ammonia is one of the most important synthetic chemical processes we have. Much of the nitrogen we use for fertilizer is "fixed" (put into usable form) through the Haber process.

$$N_2 + 3H_2 \rightarrow 2NH_3$$

Q. How many molecules of ammonium can we make from 12 molecules of nitrogen?

A. We must use a BALANCED equation. Using the BALANCED equation we relate the coefficients letting our unknown be represented by "X".

$1N_2/12$ molecules of $N_2 = 2NH_3/x$ molecules NH_3 or

$$\frac{1 \text{ N}_2 \text{ molecule}}{12 \text{ N}_2 \text{ molecules}} = \frac{2 \text{ NH}_3 \text{ molecules}}{X \text{ NH}_3 \text{ molecules}}$$

Solving for x gives

X molecules of $NH_3 = 2 NH_3 \times 12$ molecules of $N_2/ 1 N_2 = 24$ molecules of NH_3

Q. How many moles of ammonium can we make from 6 moles of hydrogen?

A. Again, using a BALANCED equation and letting "X" be the unknown number of ammonia that can be made we again set up the proportion as follows.

$3H_2/6$ moles of $H_2 = 2 NH_3/X$ moles of NH_3 or

$$\frac{3 \text{ H}_2 \text{ mole}}{6 \text{ H}_2 \text{ mole}} = \frac{2 \text{ NH}_3 \text{ mole}}{X \text{ NH}_3 \text{ mole}}$$

Again, solving for "y" we get

X moles of $NH_3 = 6$ moles $H_2 \times 2 NH_3 / 3 H_2 = 4$ moles of NH_3

Q. What weight in grams of nitrogen is necessary to make 10 grams of ammonia?

A. From the BALANCED equation we know that one mole of nitrogen gives us two moles of ammonia.

Our strategy map is

weight NH_3 → moles NH_3 → balanced equation → moles N_2 → weight N_2

First, let us calculate the number of moles of ammonia in 10 grams of ammonia.

The molecular weight (or number of grams per mole) of ammonia is

$1 N \times 14$ amu/N = 14 amu

$3H \times 1$ amu/H = 3 amu

Total = 17 amu = 17grams/mole

# of moles of ammonia is weight of ammonium/molecular weight of ammonia

moles = 10 grams/17 grams/mole = 0.59 moles.

Next, let us remember that for every two moles of ammonia we have one mole of nitrogen so the (mole) ratio of ammonia to nitrogen is 2:1. Thus, the number of moles of nitrogen necessary to make 0.59 moles of ammonia is

0.59/2 = about 0.295 mole or we can do the proportion approach

$$\frac{2\,NH_3}{0.59 \text{ moles } NH_3} = \frac{1\,N_2}{X\,N_2 \text{ moles}}$$

Solving we have X = 0.59/2 = 0.295 moles of N_2.

Now we can calculate the number of grams of nitrogen that is in 0.295 moles as follows:

Weight = gmw/mole N_2 × # moles N_2 = 28 grams/mole × 0.295 mole = 8.3 grams of nitrogen is needed to make 10 grams of ammonia.

PROPORTIONS

Many problems can be solved employing a simple proportion approach. These include reaction stoichiometry related problems, weight of an atom, density problems, etc.

Mathematically if we have

$$\frac{A}{C} = \frac{B}{D}$$

Then we can do what is called cross multiplication and set the two equal to one another. Thus AD = BC. From this all the letters can be solved by simply dividing both sides by the appropriate letter. Thus, if we want to solve for A we would divide both sides by D since division of both sides of an equivalency does not change the equivalency. Division of AD = BC by D gives A = CB/D We can do the same to solve for D giving D = CB/A and for B to give B = AD/C and for C to give C = AD/B. Thus, if we are given three of the values we can determine, solve for, the fourth value.

A similar situation exists where we are given that A = B/C. We can solve for any letter by considering that this can be rewritten as

$$\frac{A}{1} = \frac{B}{C}$$

since we can divide anything by "1" and not change the equation. We can then again cross multiple giving B = AC. Division of both sides by A gives A = B/C allowing us to solve for any of the letters given values for two of the letters. We will employ this particular form of the proportional equation approach when we deal with density.

This approach can utilized for many simple word problems. Thus, if one apple costs 50 cents ($0.50), how much would 24 apples cost. We can reword the problem as a proportion problem so that if one apple costs $0.50, 24 apples would cost how much. Mathematically this is shown as

$$\frac{\text{One apple}}{24 \text{ apples}} = \frac{\$0.50}{X \text{ dollars}}$$

We than solve for X by cross multiplication as follows

$$\text{one apple} \times X \text{ dollars} = \$0.50 \times 24 \text{ apples}$$

Division of both sides of the equation by "one apple" leaves X alone on one side of the equation and allows us to complete the solution for X.

$$\frac{\text{one apple} \times X \text{ dollars}}{\text{one apple}} = \frac{\$0.50 \times 24 \text{ apples}}{\text{one apple}}$$

leaving X cents = $0.50 × 24 apples/one apple = 12 dollars or $12.

Proportions are useful when we know all but one of the values. We will find that one mole of a material has about 6×10^{23} units and that one mole of material weights one gram formula weight. Thus we can calculate the weight of one atom of unit of a material. Thus, one mole of helium, He, weights 4 grams, its formula weight. The weight of one atom of helium is very small and can be stated in words as 6×10^{23} atoms of helium weight 4 grams, 1 atom of helium weights how many grams. In equation form this is

$$\frac{6 \times 10^{23} \text{ atoms of helium}}{1 \text{ atom of helium}} = \frac{4 \text{ grams}}{X \text{ grams}}$$

Solving for X we have X = 4 grams × 1 atom / 6×10^{23} atoms = 0.67×10^{-23} grams, or as we expected one molecule of helium weighs very little.

We can employ this proportion method to allow us to solve many problems.

REACTANT/REAGENT-THEORETICAL AND ACTUAL PERCENTAGE YIELDS

The **LIMITING REACTANT** OR **LIMITING REAGENT** is the reactant that is entirely consumed when a reaction goes to completion. It is the reactant that will limit the amount of reaction that can occur and product formed.

The possible or **THEORETICAL** or **THEORY YIELD** is the **MAXIMUM** or 100% yield that could be formed if ALL of the LIMITING REAGENT reacted, according to the balanced equation, to give products. The THEORETICAL YIELD is determined by the amounts of reactants. We employ the number of moles/molecules as the "amount"-counting factor.

Remember that we have several special "bridges" or key relationships that we need to be aware of and use as needed. It is important that you memorize these and be able to use them when appropriate.

One mole = 6×10^{23} UNITS

Number of moles = weight/gram formula weight or gram molecular weight

Road Maps/Strategy Maps for this type of problem might include

1. Weight → Moles → Bal. Eq. → Moles → Weight(which is the THEORETICAL YIELD) → Actual

2. Weight → Moles for each reactant; Then using the BALANCED EQUATION determine the LIMITING REACTANT; After the LIMITING REACTANT is determined go to Road Map 1.

QUESTION- Determine the limiting reactant if 14 grams of nitrogen and 4 grams of hydrogen are reacted to give ammonia.

ANSWER- Write BALANCED equation. $3H_2 + N_2 \rightarrow 2NH_3$

Next determine the number of moles of N_2 and H_2.

moles N_2 = weight of nitrogen divided by the molecular weight of nitrogen=

14 grams/28 g/mole = 0.5 moles

moles H_2 = weight of hydrogen divided by the molecular weight of hydrogen =

4 gram/ 2 g/mole = 2 moles

Next, remember that we need THREE moles of HYDROGEN to react with ONE mole of nitrogen. Thus, 0.5 moles of nitrogen will react with 3×0.5 moles or 1.5 moles of hydrogen. We have 2 moles of hydrogen which is GREATER than the 1.5 moles making the nitrogen the LIMITING REACTANT.

QUESTION- Given 14 g of nitrogen and 4 grams of hydrogen, what is the maximum number of moles, molecules and grams of ammonia that can be produced.

ANSWER- Above, we established the LIMITING REACTANT is nitrogen and that there was 0.5 moles of nitrogen. From the BALANCED equation, every nitrogen will give two ammonia. Thus the number of moles of ammonia theoretically possible (assuming a 100 % yield) is $2 \times 0.5 = 1$ mole of ammonia.

1 mole of ammonia $\times 6 \times 10^{23}$ molecules/mole = 6×10^{23} molecules

The weight is simply

17 g/mole ammonia $\times 1$ mole = 17 gram.

QUESTION- What is the percentage yield if only 6 grams of ammonia were produced from the reaction of 14 g of nitrogen and 4 grams of hydrogen?

ANSWER- %-Yield = (Product Wt/Theory Wt)x100 = (6/17) $\times$ 100 = 35%

QUESTION- What is the percentage yield if 32 g of methane forms 44 grams of carbon dioxide.

ANSWER- First, let us write the reaction and balance it.

Reaction-

$$CH_4 + O_2 \rightarrow CO_2 + H_2O$$

Balanced reaction

$$CH_4 + 2O_2 \rightarrow CO_2 + 2H_2O$$

Now, let us calculate the number of moles of methane in 32 g. Formula weight is 1C at 12 amu units each + 4H at 1 amu units each = 16 g/mole.

Number of moles = Weight / GFW = 32 g/ 16 g/mole = 2 moles

We now find out the number of moles of carbon dioxide that can be formed. We see in the balanced equation that for every methane molecule we get one carbon dioxide molecule, and every mole of methane produces on mole of carbon dioxide. Thus, the number of moles of carbon dioxide produced from 2 moles of methane is 2 moles.

Now let us calculate the weight of carbon dioxide that is produced. To do this we will need to know the GFW. The GFW for carbon dioxide is 1C× 12 amu/carbon plus 2O × 16 amu/oxygen = 44 g/mole.

Weight of carbon dioxide produced = number moles × GFW = 2 moles× 44 G/Mole = 88 grams and this is the theoretical yield.

The percentage yield is the actual yield over the theoretical yield and that value times 100 to convert it to percentage.

% Yield = (44 grams produced/88 grams theoretical yield) × 100 = 50%.

LAWS OF THERMODYNAMICS

There are at least four laws of thermodynamics but only three are generally mentioned. These laws are often said to be "self evident" and evolved through observing the world we live in. The **first law of thermodynamics** says essentially that energy flows downhill. Thus, when we hold a snowball our hand become colder and the snowball melts. Energy (heat is a form of energy) flows from something of higher energy to something of lower energy; or in terms of temperature as a measure of heat, from an object of higher temperature, our hand, to something of lower temperature, the snowball. The flow of energy is often measured in a term called **enthalpy**.

A chemical reaction such as neutralization and combustion are both very exothermic reactions and by agreement we say that the enthalpy is negative. The more exothermic a reaction is the higher the negative enthalpy value is for the reaction. Conversely, the more endothermic the higher the positive value for enthalpy

The **second law of thermodynamics** is expressed by many pithy sayings such as "things go from bad to worse" and "order decreases." The formal measure of order is called **entropy**. It is said that entropy is times arrow meaning that in our world and universe that there is a constant drive towards a more random world, universe.

The **third law of thermodynamics** says that at absolute zero temperature that there is no movement.

In reactions we often talk about driving forces. There are many such as the formation of a solid drives reactions to completion and the formation of molecules drives reactions to completion.

The formation of a precipitate involves the formation of a solid so that most precipitations go almost completely. The formation of water, a molecule, from the reaction of an acid and base also often goes to near completion.

PROBLEMS

1. The reaction between fluorine gas and methane, CH_4, can be described as below. Write the balanced reaction for this reaction.

2. What is the significance/importance of a balanced equation?

3. What does a reaction with a 100 % yield mean?

4. In the drawing below, how many carbon tetrafluoride molecules can be made?

5. In the drawing above, what reactant is in excess? How much in excess is it?

6. Most nitrogen is fixed, put into a usable form for plants to use, by lightening. Commercially, most of our nitrogen is put into a usable form, ammonia, by the reaction of nitrogen and hydrogen. Write and balance the equation showing the formation of ammonia.

7. How many molecules of ammonia can be made from 6 molecules of hydrogen?

8. How many moles of nitrogen are needed to form 20 moles of ammonia from an excess of hydrogen.

9. How many grams of nitrogen can be reacted with 12 moles of hydrogen to form ammonia?

10. How many grams of ammonia can be made from 24 grams of hydrogen from reaction with an excess of nitrogen?

11. How many moles of ammonia can be made from 2 moles of nitrogen and 4 moles of hydrogen?

12. What is the percentage yield if 24 grams of hydrogen were reacted with an excess of nitrogen to form 100 grams of ammonia?

13. What weight of nickel IV sulfide is needed to make 50 grams of sulfur dioxide according to the following balanced equation?

$$2NiS_2 + 5O_2 \rightarrow 2NiO + 4SO_2$$

14. How many moles of carbon dioxide are made from burning 20 moles of octane in an automobile engine?

15. How much carbon dioxide is made from burning 20 moles of octane?

16. How many moles of methane, CH_4, are needed to produce 1.2×10^{24} molecules of carbon dioxide?

17. Photosynthesis can be thought of as the reverse of combustion in that complex molecules, often saccharides and eventually polysaccharides are produced from carbon dioxide and water. How many molecules of carbon dioxide are required to produce 1 mole of glucose, $C_6H_{12}O_6$?

    The non-balanced equation is

$$CO_2 + H_2O \rightarrow C_6H_{12}O_6$$

18. What is the theoretical yield?

19. What is the limiting reactant or limiting reagent?

20. What is the actual yield?

21. Give an example of the second law of thermodynamics in action.

22. For the decomposition of dinitrogen pentaoxide into nitrogen dioxide and oxygen how many moles of oxygen are produced from the decomposition of 10 moles of dinitrogen pentaoxide?

23. Hydrazine, N_2H_4, has been used as a fuel in our space program. It decomposes explosively into ammonia and nitrogen gas. How many molecules of nitrogen and ammonia are formed from the decomposition on a single molecule of hydrazine?

    The reaction is exothermic. The rate of reactions increases with increased temperature. Comment on how hydrazine might be a good fuel.

24. The reaction of aluminum with oxygen to form aluminum oxide occurs very slowly. How many moles of aluminum oxide is formed from the reaction of 100 grams of aluminum and an excess of oxygen?

25. Why are so called road maps or solution maps useful?

26. According to the neutralization reaction between potassium hydroxide and sulfuric acid how many moles of sulfuric acid are neutralized by 10 moles of potassium hydroxide?

27. According to the reaction between silver nitrate and potassium bromide how many moles of silver bromide can be produced from 15 moles of silver nitrate?

28. How many moles of sodium hydroxide, gfw = 40 g/mole, are in 200 grams of sodium hydroxide.?

29. Write a balanced equation if we know that a single carbon atom reacts with two chlorine molecules forming carbon tetrachloride.

30. Write a solution map or road map for determining the weight of carbon dioxide product that can be formed from 200 grams of butane, C_4H_{10}.

31. Write the balanced equation for the combustion of butane, C_3H_8.

32. How many moles of carbon dioxide can be produced from combusting 3 moles of propane, C_3H_8.

34. For the proportion used in problem 33 what are the units for each chemical?

35. Aspirin, $C_9H_8O_4$, is often made by reacting acetic anhydride, $C_4H_6O_3$ with salicylic acid, $C_7H_6O_3$ forming aspirin and acetic acid, $C_2H_4O_2$. How many moles of aspirin can be made from 18 moles of salicylic acid and an excess of acetic anhydride?

ANSWERS

1. The reaction between fluorine gas and methane, CH4, can be described as below. Write the balanced reaction for this reaction.

We notice that we have a complete reaction with no reactants remaining. Thus, we can deduce the ratio of reactants and products by simply noting the number of each compound on each side of the arrow.

On the reactant side we have $4CH_4$ and $8F_2$ and on the product side we have $4CF_4$ and $8H_2$ or

$$4CH_4 + 8F_2 \rightarrow 4CF_4 + 8H_2$$

and dividing the coefficients by four gives us the balanced equation with the smallest ratio of coefficients.

$$CH_4 + 2F_2 \rightarrow CF_4 + 2H_2$$

2. What is the significance/importance of a balanced equation?

The coefficients connect the ratios of the various reactants and products. Thus, above every methane molecule reacts with two fluorine molecules to give one carbon tetrafluoride and two hydrogen molecules. This ratio of 1:2 → 1:2 is critical in understanding and designing chemical reactions.

3. What does a reaction with a 100 % yield mean?

If all of the reactants react then we will have only the products remaining and a 100% yield. This is often referred to as the theoretical yield or maximum yield. Generally, in real situations we get less than 100% reaction or 100% yield of product.

4. In the drawing below, how many carbon tetrafluoride molecules can be made?

Though we doubled the methane molecules from the picture given in problem 1 we are still limited by the number of fluorine molecules to produce only four carbon tetrafluoride molecules. In this situation, the number of carbon tetrafluorides produced is limited by the number of fluorine molecules. Thus, fluorine, in this case, is referred to as the limiting agent or limiting reagent. We notice that on the product side we have four unreacted methane molecules. Methane is then the reactant or reagent in excess.

5. In the drawing above, what reactant is in excess? How much in excess is it?

We notice that on the product side we have four unreacted methane molecules. Methane is then the reactant or reagent in excess.

We normally do not show in our chemical equation what is in excess or limiting or how much in excess the chemical is but focus on the reactants that react in the ratio shown by the coefficients in the balanced equation. But, sometimes we may be asked to tell how much of a reactant might remain after a reaction goes to completion assuming a 100% or total yield. Sometimes we might also add an excess of a reagent if needed.

6. Most nitrogen is fixed, put into a usable form for plants to use, by lightening. Commercially, most of our nitrogen is put into a usable form, ammonia, by the reaction of nitrogen and hydrogen. Write and balance the equation showing the formation of ammonia.

$$N_2 + H_2 \rightarrow NH_3$$

The balanced reaction is

$$N_2 + 3H_2 \rightarrow 2NH_3$$

7. How many molecules of ammonia can be made from 6 molecules of hydrogen?

   There are several ways to work this type of problem. We will use a proportion approach based on the balanced equation and what is given in the problem. Thus, we know that $2 NH_3$ are made from $3H_2$ from the coefficients in the balanced equations. We are asked in the question how many NH_3 (XNH_3 where X is the unknown we are trying to determine) are formed from 6 molecules of H_2. This is expressed by proportion as follows

   $$\frac{2NH_3}{XNH_3} = \frac{3H_2}{6 \text{ molecules of } H_2}$$

   Cross multiplication and solving for X gives

   $$X \, NH_3 \times 3H_2 = 2NH_3 \times 6H_2 \text{ and}$$

   $$XNH_3 = 2NH_3 \times 6H_2/3H_2 = 4NH_3 \text{ molecules}$$

   In these questions, generally a percentage yield of 100% is assumed. This yield is often referred to as the theoretical yield or maximum theoretical yield.

8. How many moles of nitrogen are needed to form 20 moles of ammonia from an excess of hydrogen.

   We have the same balanced equation.

   $$N_2 + 3H_2 \rightarrow 2NH_3$$

   Again, using the same proportion approach we get

   $$\frac{2NH_3}{20NH_3} = \frac{N_2}{XN_2}$$

   Solving for X through cross multiplication we get 2X = 20 and X = 10 moles of nitrogen are needed to form 20 moles of ammonium.

   The road map for problems 7 and 8 are

   molecules $\rightarrow$ balanced equation coefficients $\rightarrow$ molecules and

   moles $\rightarrow$ balanced equation coefficients $\rightarrow$ moles

   But not directly weight $\rightarrow$ balanced equation $\rightarrow$ weight.

9. How many grams of nitrogen can be reacted with 12 moles of hydrogen to form ammonia?

   Again we use the same balanced equation.

   $$N_2 + 3H_2 \rightarrow 2NH_3$$

   We will again use a similar road map that describes the steps we need to carry out to arrive at the correct answer.

   For this problem it is

   moles hydrogen $\rightarrow$ balanced equation $\rightarrow$ moles nitrogen $\rightarrow$ weight nitrogen

We set up our proportion again based on the balanced equation and data given in the problem as follows.

$$\frac{3H_2}{12H_2} = \frac{1N_2}{XN_2}$$

Solving for XN_2 we get

$XN_2 \times 3H_2 = 12H_2 \times 1N_2$

and $XN_2 = 12H_2 \times 1N_2/3H_2$

and $X = 4$ moles of nitrogen.

We now need to calculate the weight that is 4 moles of nitrogen.

Weight = # Moles $\times$ GFW = 4 moles $\times$ 28 g/mole = 112 g.

10. How many grams of ammonia can be made from 24 grams of hydrogen from reaction with an excess of nitrogen?

   Again, we use the same balanced equation

$$N_2 + 3H_2 \rightarrow 2NH_3$$

   Our solution map is

   weight of hydrogen $\rightarrow$ moles hydrogen $\rightarrow$ balanced equation $\rightarrow$ moles ammonia $\rightarrow$ weight ammonia

   For brevity we often write this out as simply

   wt $\rightarrow$ moles $\rightarrow$ balanced eq $\rightarrow$ moles $\rightarrow$ weight

   We also often omit many of the units but we need to remember that the units are critical and need to know what those units really are.

   We begin by calculating the number of moles of hydrogen in 24 grams

   moles = wt/gfw = 24 g/2 g/mole = 12 moles of hydrogen.

   The proportion is then

$$\frac{2NH_3}{XNH_3} = \frac{3H_2}{12H_2}$$

   Solving for $X = 2 \times 12/3 = 8$ moles of ammonia

   Wt of ammonia = 8 moles $\times$ 17 g/mole = 136 grams of ammonia.

11. How many moles of ammonia can be made from 2 moles of nitrogen and 4 moles of hydrogen?

   It is important to recognize both how to solve problems, the tools you have at hand to do this, and what kind of problem you are being challenged with. Problems 1 and 7 are referred to as a molecule-molecule problems since you are given molecules of one chemical and asked for the number of molecules of another molecule with both molecules connected by a BALANCED equation. REMEMBER that the coefficients connect the number of molecules to one another in a BALANCED equation.

   The problem in question 11 is similar to the problems 1 and 7 except here we are using MOLES and not molecules. Problems 3 and 4 are referred to as weight-mole (problems 8 and 9) and weight-weight problems (problem 4). Problem 11 is referred to as a LIMITING AGENT or LIMITING REAGENT type of problem. It takes the longest time to solve of these types of problems so in an exam be sure to do the shorter problems first and then tackle the problems that take longer to do.

One way to approach the limiting reagent problem is to simply do two problems, one related to one of the weights and the second one related to the second weight given and then determining which produces the least amount of the product and that chemical is referred to as the limiting agent.

There are more difficult problems such as ones that ask how much of a reagent remains after the limiting agent is fully consumed. We will not do this type of problem here but be prepared to do so if directed to do so.

Again, the same balanced equation is used.

$$N_2 + 3H_2 \rightarrow 2NH_3$$

First, let us take how much ammonia can be made from 2 moles of nitrogen. We can create the following proportion.

$$\frac{2NH_3}{XNH_3} = \frac{1N_2}{2N_2}$$

Cross multiplication and solving for X we get $X = 2 \times 2/1 = 4$ moles of NH_3.

Second, we will now see how much can be formed from 4 moles of hydrogen. We can create the proportion as below.

$$\frac{2NH_3}{XNH_3} = \frac{3H_2}{4H_2}$$

Cross multiplication and solving for X gives $X = 4 \times 2/3 = 2.7$ moles of ammonia.

We now ask the question, which will give us the least amount of ammonia, or which is less 2.7 or 4. The answer is obviously 2.7 which is the amount of ammonia that we can get from 4 moles of hydrogen. So, we have the yield, 2.7 moles, and the limiting agent, hydrogen.

What is the weight of 2.7 moles of ammonia. The weight is calculated from

Wt = # moles $\times$ gfw = 2.7 moles $\times$ 17 g/mole = 46 g of ammonia.

The 17 g/mole is simply the formula weight of ammonia.

1N $\times$ 14 amu/N = 14 amu

3H $\times$ 1 amu/H = 3 amu

Total = 17 amu or 17 g/mole

12. What is the percentage yield if 24 grams of hydrogen were reacted with an excess of nitrogen to form 100 grams of ammonia?

In problem 10 we calculated that we could make, the maximum yield, the theoretical yield, 136 grams of ammonia.

% Yield = (Actual yield/Theoretical yield) $\times$ 100 = (100 g/136 g) $\times$ 100 = 74%.

The 100 grams is the actual weight of ammonia that was collected. The "actual yield" will be given in these kind of problems.

13. What weight of nickel IV sulfide is needed to make 50 grams of sulfur dioxide according to the following balanced equation?

$$2NiS_2 + 5O_2 \rightarrow 2NiO + 4SO_2$$

This kind of problem is a weight-weight problem where we are given the weight of sodium dioxide and asked how much nickel IV sulfide is needed to make, in theory, this amount.

The gfw of silicon dioxide is

$1S \times 32$ amu/Si = 32 amu

$2O \times 16$ amu/O = 32 amu

GFW = 64 amu = 64 g/mole

moles of sulfur dioxide = wt/gfw = 50 g/64 g/mole = 0.78 moles

$$\frac{2NiS_2}{XNiS_2} = \frac{4SO_2}{0.78\ SO_2}$$

$X = 2 \times 0.78/4 = 0.39$ moles of NiS_2

$1Ni \times 58.7$ amu/Ni = 58.7 amu

$2\ S \times 32$ amu/S = 64 amu

Total = 122.7 amu = 122.7 g/mole

Wt = # moles $\times$ gfw = 0.39 moles of $NiS_2 \times 122.7$ g/mole = 48 g.

14. How many moles of carbon dioxide are made from burning 20 moles of octane in an automobile **engine?**

First, we need to write the equation that describes the combustion of the octane. We remember that the major products of burning (combustion) of hydrocarbons and compounds with C, H, and O are carbon dioxide and water. Octane is a hydrocarbon, containing only carbon and hydrogen so carbon dioxide and water are the major products.

$$C_8H_{18} + O_2 \rightarrow CO_2 + H_2O$$

The balanced equation is

$$C_8H_{18} + 12.5\ O_2 \rightarrow 8CO_2 + 9H_2O$$

$$2C_8H_{18} + 25O_2 \rightarrow 16CO_2 + 18H_2O$$

An appropriate proportion is then

$$\frac{2C_8H_{18}}{20C_8H_{18}} = \frac{16CO_2}{XCO_2}$$

$X = 20 \times 16/2 = 160$ moles.

15. How much carbon dioxide is made from burning 20 moles of octane?

From problem 14 we determined that 160 moles of carbon dioxide were formed

$1C \times 12$ amu/C = 12 amu

$2O \times 16$ amu/O = 32 amu

Total = 44 amu = 44 g/mole

Weight = # moles $\times$ gfw = 160 moles $\times$ 44 g/mole = 7040 g = 7×10^3 grams.

16. How many moles of methane, CH_4, are needed to produce 1.2×10^{24} molecules of carbon dioxide?

First, always balance the general reaction.

$$CH_4 + O_2 \rightarrow CO_2 + H_2O$$

Balanced this equation is

$$CH_4 + 2O_2 \rightarrow CO_2 + 2H_2O$$

1.2×10^{24} molecules/6×10^{23} molecules/mole = 2 moles carbon dioxide.

The question is then how many moles of methane are needed to produce 2 moles of carbon dioxide?

This problem represents a special case where the coefficients for the two compounds/element are the same, here both of the coefficients for methane and carbon dioxide are one. Thus, 2 moles of carbon dioxide are produced from 2 moles of methane.

17. Photosynthesis can be thought of as the reverse of combustion in that complex molecules, often saccharides and eventually polysaccharides are produced from carbon dioxide and water. How many molecules of carbon dioxide are required to produce 1 mole of glucose, $C_6H_{12}O_6$?
The non-balanced equation is

$$CO_2 + H_2O \rightarrow C_6H_{12}O_6$$

Balanced it is

$$6CO_2 + 6H_2O \rightarrow C_6H_{12}O_6 + 6O_2$$

The appropriate proportion is

$$\frac{6CO_2}{XCO_2} = \frac{1C_6H_{12}O_6}{1C_6H_{12}O_6}$$

Cross multiplication and solving for X = 6 moles of CO_2.

The number of molecules is related to the number of moles through Avogadro's number such that

molecules = # moles × AV# = # moles × 6×10^{23} molecules/mole = 6 moles × 6×10^{23} = 36×10^{23} = 3.6×10^{24}.

18. What is the theoretical yield?

Theoretical yield is the maximum yield; the 100% yield.

19. What is the limiting reactant or limiting reagent?

It is the reactant that is totally consumed in a reaction.

20. What is the actual yield?

The actual yield is the real yield produced.

21. Give an example of the second law of thermodynamics in action.

A clean room become messy if we do not work at keeping it clean, thus the general tendency is to go from a clean, ordered room to a messy room. A box full of pennies that are all heads up will become a mixture of heads up and tails up when shaken.

22. For the decomposition of dinitrogen pentaoxide into nitrogen dioxide and oxygen how many moles of oxygen are produced from the decomposition of 10 moles of dinitrogen pentaoxide?

First, write the overall equation and then balance it.

$$N_2O_5 \rightarrow NO_2 + O_2$$

Balanced this is

$$2N_2O_5 \rightarrow 4NO_2 + O_2$$

The proportion is

$$\frac{2N_2O_5}{10N_2O_5} = \frac{1O_2}{XO_2}$$

$X = 10 \times 1/2 = 5$ moles of oxygen are produced.

23. Hydrazine, N_2H_4, has been used as a fuel in our space program. It decomposes explosively into ammonia and nitrogen gas. How many molecules of nitrogen and ammonia are formed from the decomposition on a single molecule of hydrazine?

The reaction is exothermic. The rate of reactions increases with increased temperature. Comment on how hydrazine might be a good fuel.

The overall reaction is

$$N_2H_4 \rightarrow NH_3 + N_2$$

The balanced equation is

$$3N_2H_4 \rightarrow 4NH_3 + N_2$$

Divide all the coefficients by 3 to get

$$N_2H_4 \rightarrow 4/3\ NH_3 + 1/3N_2$$

Thus, one molecule of hydrazine produces $4/3 + 1/3$ or $5/3$ molecules of gas.

Since the reaction is exothermic, as the reaction progresses it produces more heat which in turn makes the reaction to go faster leading to an explosive reaction. The amount of gas produced is great considering that hydrazine itself is a liquid or solid depending on the conditions of the reaction. Thus, lots of gas is produced acting as thrust for the rocket. The volume of a single mole of liquid or solid hydrazine is about 20 mL but the volume for a single mole of gas is about 22,000 mL under room conditions of temperature and pressure.

24. The reaction of aluminum with oxygen to form aluminum oxide occurs very slowly. How many moles of aluminum oxide is formed from the reaction of 100 grams of aluminum and an excess of oxygen?

The reaction is

$$Al + O_2 \rightarrow Al_2O_3$$

Balanced this is

$$4Al + 3O_2 \rightarrow 2Al_2O_3$$

Our solution strategy map is weight aluminum → moles aluminum → balanced equation → moles aluminum oxide → weight of aluminum oxide

moles = wt/gfw or in this case it is # moles = wt/atomic weight = 100 g/27g/mole = 3.7 moles

The needed proportion is

$$\frac{4Al}{3.7Al} = \frac{2Al_2O_3}{XAl_2O_3}$$

Solving for X = 3.7 × 2/4 = 1.9 moles.

2Al × 27amu/Al = 54 amu

3O × 16 amu/O = 48 amu

Total = 102 amu = 102 g/mole

Weight of aluminum oxide is 1.9 moles × 102 g/mole = 190 grams = 1.9×10^2 grams.

25. Why are so called road maps or solution maps useful?

They tell what we need to do and in the order we need to do them.

26. According to the neutralization reaction between potassium hydroxide and sulfuric acid how many moles of sulfuric acid are neutralized by 10 moles of potassium hydroxide?

$$KOH + H_2SO_4 \rightarrow K_2SO_4 + H_2O$$

Balanced this is

$$2KOH + H_2SO_4 \rightarrow K_2SO_4 + 2H_2O$$

The coefficients for KOH and H_2SO_4 are 2:1. We can either simply think that the ratio of KOH to H_2SO_4 is 2:1 so 10:5 so the moles of sulfuric acid neutralized by 10 moles of potassium hydroxide is 5. We can also use the proportion method.

27. According to the reaction between silver nitrate and potassium bromide how many moles of silver bromide can be produced from 15 moles of silver nitrate?

The starting and balanced reaction are the same and is

$$AgNO_3 + KBr \rightarrow AgBr + KNO_3$$

Since the coefficients for $AgNO_3$ and AgBr are the same, here both one, the number of moles of AgBr produced is the same as the number of moles of $AgNO_3$ assuming that the silver nitrate is the limiting agent. Thus, 15 moles can be produced.

28. How many moles of sodium hydroxide, gfw = 40 g/mole, are in 200 grams of sodium hydroxide.?

moles = wt/gfw = 200 g/40 g/mole = 5 moles.

29. Write a balanced equation if we know that a single carbon atom reacts with two chlorine molecules forming carbon tetrachloride.

$$C + 2Cl_2 \rightarrow CCl_4$$

30. Write a solution map or road map for determining the weight of carbon dioxide product that can be formed from 200 grams of butane, C_4H_{10}.

gfw butane →moles butane → balanced equation →moles carbon dioxide → wt carbon dioxide

31. Write the balanced equation for the combustion of butane, C_3H_8.

$$C_3H_8 + O_2 \rightarrow CO_2 + H_2O$$

Balanced it is

$$C_3H_8 + 5O_2 \rightarrow 3CO_2 + 4H_2O$$

32. How many moles of carbon dioxide can be produced from combusting 3 moles of propane, C_3H_8.

Using the balanced equation given above allows us to write the following proportion.

$$\frac{1\,C_3H_8}{3C_3H_8} = \frac{3CO_2}{XCO_2}$$

X = 3 × 3 = 9 moles of carbon dioxide.

33. What weight of carbon dioxide is produced from combustion of 3 moles of propane, C_3H_8.

From above we determined that 9 moles of carbon dioxide were produced.

1C × 12 amu/C = 12 amu

2O × 16 amu/O = 32 amu

Total = 44 amu = 44 g/mole

Wt = # moles × gfw = 9 moles × 44 g/mole = 396 g

34. For the proportion used in problem 33 what are the units for each chemical?

We often use the proportion and describe it briefly for economy of space and time, but it is important that we understand that each of these have units. Here they are simple as follows.

$$\frac{1\,C_3H_8 \text{ moles}}{3C_3H_8 \text{ moles}} = \frac{3CO_2 \text{ moles}}{XCO_2 \text{ moles}}$$

Also, remember that there are other ways to do these problems. Learn the approach that makes sense to you and that is allowed by your teacher.

35. Aspirin, $C_9H_8O_4$, is often made by reacting acetic anhydride, $C_4H_6O_3$ with salicylic acid, $C_7H_6O_3$ forming aspirin and acetic acid, $C_2H_4O_2$. How many moles of aspirin can be made from 18 moles of salicylic acid and an excess of acetic anhydride?

First, the balanced equation.

$$C_4H_6O_3 + C_7H_6O_3 \rightarrow C_9H_8O_4 + C_2H_4O_2$$

We notice that all of the reactants and products have the same coefficient, in this case it is one. Thus, the number of moles of aspirin is the number of moles of salicylic acid, 18 moles.

SAMPLE TEST PROBLEMS

Name _____ Date _____

Circle only correct answers.

36. How many moles of methanol, CH_3OH, must be combusted to give 8 moles of carbon dioxide?

a. 2; b. 4; c. 8; d. 12; e. 1.

37. How many grams of methanol, CH_3OH, must be burned to give 72 grams of water?

a. 32; b. 64; c. 96; d. 128; e. 16.

38. How many molecules of water are formed from the reaction of one mole of methanol, CH_3OH?

a. 3×10^{23}; b. 6×10^{23}; c. 18; d. 1.2×10^{24}; e. 36.

39. How many moles of water can be made from the burning of 2 moles of ethanol, CH_3OH with five moles of molecular oxygen, O_2?

a. 1; b. 2; c. 3; d. 4; e. 6.7.

40. How many moles of pentane, C_5H_{12}, are there in 36 grams of pentane.

a. 0.5; b. 1; c. 2; d. 4; e. 8.

41. What is the theoretical yield, in grams, of water produced in burning 18 grams of hydrogen, H_2, in excess oxygen, O_2?

a. 36; b. 82; c. 93; d. 45; e. 162.

42. What is the percentage yield if 18 grams of hydrogen, H_2, burned in excess oxygen gave 108 grams of water?

a. 22; b. 33; c. 44; d. 67; e. 87.

43. What coefficient must be in front of oxygen to balance the following reaction?

$$NiS_2 + O_2 \rightarrow NiO + SO_2$$

a. 1; b. 2; c. 3; d. 4; e. 5.

44. Given the following balanced equation, how many moles of carbon, C, are needed to make 8 moles of carbon monoxide?

$$SiO_2 + 3C \rightarrow SiC + 2CO$$

a. 12; b. 8; c. 6; d. 4; e. 2.

45. How many molecules of water molecules are in 9 grams of water?

a. 1×10^{23}; b. 3×10^{23}; c. 6×10^{23}; d. 27; e. 0.5.

Quantum Mechanics and the Periodic Table

ELECTRONS AND BONDING

Interestingly, even though we have three subatomic particles, only the outer electrons are dealt with extensively in chemistry. Why? Because it is the sharing and loss/gain of these electrons that form chemical bonds. Bonding can be of two kinds- **ionic** bonding where electrons are **lost** by one atom and **gained** by another; and **covalent** bonding-where electrons are **shared** between two atoms.

WAVE NATURE OF LIGHT

We have not seen an electron but have seen its actions.

Light is a form of energy,E, and is described in terms of wavelength, λ, and frequency, ν, as

$$E = h\nu \text{ and } \nu = c/\lambda \text{ and substitution gives } E = hc/\lambda.$$

Wavelength, λ, is the distance between any two adjacent identical points of a wave-unit of length such as meters or nanometers. **Frequency, ν,** is the number of wavelengths of a wave that passes a fixed point in one unit of time such as the number/ second is called hertz (Hz). "h" = Plank's constant, c = velocity of light.

You need to know that as energy increases, frequency increases- that is, energy and frequency are directly related; and that as energy increases, wavelength decreases- that is, energy and wavelength are **inversely** or **"indirectly related." "Directly related"** means that as one increases the other increases; and as one decreases the other decreases. Inversely related means that as one increases the other does the opposite, decreases. And as one decreases the other increases. What is the relationship between frequency and wavelength?

LIGHT

Light is continuous ranging from high energy gamma and X-ray to low energy radio, radar, and microwaves. This continuum is often called the **Electromagnetic Spectrum.**

As scientists were striking atoms with various particles and energies, they found

*that only selected, certain, specific energies were being "accepted" (absorbed)

*that only certain, specific energies were being "given off" (emitted)

Einstein and others reasoned that light was not simply a continuous wave but rather could be also described as possessing bundles or quanta of photons or particles of electromagnetic energy.

From this, and many other observations, the Bohr theory of the hydrogen atom was developed. The essentials of the Bohr theory was later transferred to other atoms. While no longer a current theory, many of the aspects of the Bohr atom are still correct. Two important aspects of the Bohr atomic theory that are still used are as follow:

*electrons have only certain, specific energy values in an atom. These allowed energy values are called **ENERGY LEVELS** and they correspond to the selected, specific energies that experimentally were found to be absorbed or emitted.

*electrons can move from one energy level to another when they accept (absorb; moving from an inner to an outer or further away from the nucleus energy level) or emit (moving from an outer to an inner or closer to the nucleus energy level). They cannot move to ½ or 1/3 between the energy levels but must move between one and another energy level. Absorption occurs when the correct energy is taken on to move an electron from a lower energy to a higher energy level. Emission of energy occurs when the correct energy is given off as an electron moves from a higher energy level to a lower energy level. This "correct energy" corresponds to the difference in energy between the two energy levels.

Several ideas came forth as scientists were studying the effect of light on various elements. These were-

1. Light moves at a constant speed-the speed of light-3×10^8 m/s. Energy differences are not related to speed but to frequency and the wavelength of the light. Light has both wave (frequency, wavelength) and particle (bundles) properties.

2. Planck believed that atoms in a solid oscillated or vibrated with a specific frequency and that these vibrating atoms could only have certain energies that were described by

   $E = nh\nu$ where n = 1,2,3, ... And h = Plank's constant.

3. Bohr's model was "one dimensional" whereas the Quantum Mechanical Model is three dimensional. Bohr's model concentrated on hydrogen and the Principle Quantum Number "n" . In Quantum Mechanics, "n" is called the Principle Quantum Number and it describes the general distance and energy electrons within a "shell" are from the nucleus.

Heisenberg showed that is was impossible to know both the **exact** energy and **exact** location. This is called the **Heisenberg Uncertainty Principle**. Quantum Mechanics selected to know the exact energy and let the location be known in a probability manner. Thus, we give the locations of electrons in probability terms calling such locations orbitals. As a side note, we were told that we could not see atoms because of the uncertainty principle, yet today we can "see" them. How is this possible?

QUANTUM NUMBERS

There are four quantum numbers similar to an address in a letter to Albert as follows:

Dr. Albert Einstein
322 Cottage Street
Princeton, NJ 08540

There are four locators, beginning with the most general NJ → Princeton → 322 Cottage Street → and finally to the specific person, Albert. See how the four quantum numbers are similar to Albert's address.

To describe the (probable) location about an atomic nucleus we use FOUR quantum numbers. The combination of these four quantum numbers allows us to describe the probable location and shape of the orbital of each electron in an atom. This probability location or "wave function" of the electron is called an **Atomic Orbital**. We define the atomic orbital as the probability path taken by an electron and this atomic orbital is defined by a unique set of four quantum numbers.

These four quantum numbers are a series of values each one describing one aspect of the atomic orbital. They are described following.

1. **Principle quantum number**- given the symbol "n"; it describes the **"general" distance** from the nucleus that the particular electron resides. Each value is either a small whole number, starting with 1, or a capital letter beginning with K. The numerical values must be **small whole positive numbers** and as the values increase, the electron, on the average, resides further from the nucleus. Each single principle quantum number describes a "shell."

Numeral value	1	2	3	4	5	6	....
Letter value	K	L	M	N	O	P	....

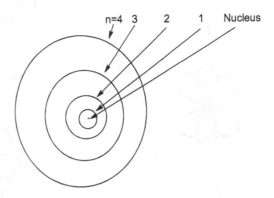

This is the same quantum number that Bohr used in his relationship $E = nh\nu$.

Electrons with the same principle quantum number are said to be in the same shell. Notice that the values of all four quantum numbers are interrelated.

2. **Angular momentum quantum number**- is the second quantum number and given the symbol of "l". This is also sometimes referred to as the **secondary quantum number**. It gives the general **shape** of the orbital. Values are again given in two formats. First, values are gotten from the principle quantum number with the highest, and furthest away from the nucleus, being "n – 1" but beginning with "0", i.e., **l = n – 1 ....0**. They are also given in small letters.

Angular momentum quantum numbers

numeral value	letter
0	s
1	p
2	d
3	f
4	g
5	h

Each of these angular momentum quantum numbers corresponds to what is called a "**subshell**." A subshell is a grouping of similar shaped orbitals. The "s" type orbitals are spherical (hence the "s"); "p" type of orbitals are dumbbell shaped and most of the "d" types of orbitals are clover leafed in shape.

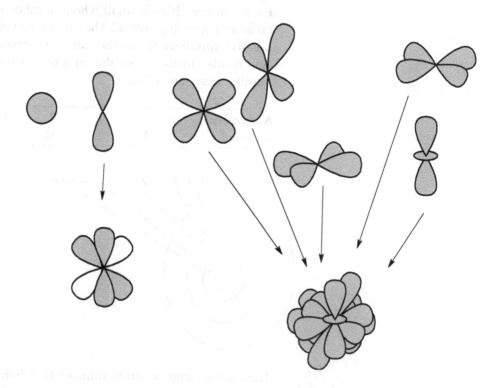

For each shell there is one "s" orbital and can be three "p" orbitals each set at right angles to one another forming a sphere with bumps on it. Each "p" orbital has two lobes as seen above. There can be five "d" orbitals with four of them having four lobs and the fifth described as a "p" orbitals with a doughnut section at the juncture of the two lobes. Notice that the combination of all five "d" orbitals again approaches a sphere with bumps on it. We will learn that each orbital can have 1 or 2 electrons within it.

The shapes are probability contours. Often 90, 95, or 99 % contours are given meaning that 90, 95, or 99 % of the time the electron should be found within this volume.

We often use the combination of the principle and secondary quantum numbers to designate a particular **subshell**. Thus, an electron in the second shell and within the "O" or "s" subshell is called a "2s" electron. Similarity, an electron in the third shell with a subshell value of "1" corresponding to a "p" type of orbital is described as a "3p" electron.

3. The third quantum number is the magnetic quantum number designated by "m_i". It tells us the **number of orbitals** within each subshell. These orbitals are pictured above. Since we will shortly find out that each orbital can have 1 or 2 electrons we know the maximum number of electrons that can be in each kind of orbital, i.e., subshell.

   The values for m_i are derived from "l" so that $m_i = +/- 1 \ldots\ldots 0$. Thus, for "l" = 3 we have for $m_i = +/- 3, +/-2, +/-1, 0$ or $-3, -2, -1, 0, 1, 2, 3$ for a total of 7 orbitals or a maximum 14 electrons (7 orbitals times 2 electrons/orbital). Also, for "l" = 3, we are talking about "f" orbitals.

4. The fourth quantum number is called the spin quantum number and it specifies a **specific electron** and is given the symbol m_s. Values are $m_s = +/- \frac{1}{2}$ or $+ \frac{1}{2}$ and $-\frac{1}{2}$. or simply $\frac{1}{2}$ and $-\frac{1}{2}$. Thus, within a single orbital we can have one electron with a $\frac{1}{2}$ spin and a second with a $-\frac{1}{2}$ for a total of two electrons per orbital.

   The Pauli Exclusion Principle states that no two electrons in the same atom can have the same set of four quantum numbers.

   Summary: There are four quantum numbers. Each electron in every atom has its on unique set of four quantum numbers. The Pauli Exclusion Principle states that no two electrons in the same atom can have the same four quantum numbers. Each of these four quantum numbers tells something different about an electron. The principle number, n, tells the average distance that the electron resides from the nucleus of the atom. It has values of 1,2,3,4,5, … but not zero and the larger the n number the further away from the nucleus the electron is. Each "n" value is called a **shell**. The secondary quantum number, l, tells the shape of the probable orbital. It has values of n−1 down to zero. (In quantum numbers, zero is a value and does not mean nothing.) Each "l" value is a **subshell**. These "l" values have two names, one a number that does include zero, and a small letter. We need to know both so that when we are given one we can give the second, so for l = 0 we are talking about "s" electrons and when we are talking about "p" electrons l = 1.

l =	0	1	2	3	4	5	6	……
	s	p	d	f	g	h	I	……
Shape	spherical	2-lobed	clover leafed					

The third quantum number, m_l, gives the orientation in space that each of these orbitals have and consequently tells the number of each type of orbital. m_l values are $+/-1$ ..... 0. Thus, for $l = 3$ we have $+/-3$, $+/-2$, $+/-1$, and 0 or -3, -2, -1, 0, $+1$, $+2$, $+3$ or five orbitals. Each "l" values describes an **orbital**. Thus, whenever we have a combination of the principle quantum number with the secondary quantum number, like 2s, we know that there is one 2s orbital. For a 4d combination we have a possible 5 orbitals in the "n" shell.

The fourth quantum number, spin quantum number, m_s, has a value of either $+\frac{1}{2}$ or $-\frac{1}{2}$. This is often written as $+/-\frac{1}{2}$. This gives the maximum number of electrons that can be in any orbital. From this we can deduce the number of possible s, p, d, f, ... electrons in a given subshell.

$l =$	0	1	2	3	4	5	6	....
	s	p	d	f	g	h	i	....
# Orbitals	1	3	5	7	9	11	13	
Max. # Electrons	2	6	10	14	18	22	26	

Following is a brief summary of possible values for first three principle quantum numbers.

n	l(type orbital)	mi	# orbitals/max. # electrons
1	0(s)	0	1/2
2	0(s)	0	1/2
2	1(p)	$+/-1,0$	3/6
3	0(s)	0	1/2
3	1(p)	$+/-1,0$	3/6
3	2(d)	$+/-2,+/-1,0$	5/10

ELECTRONIC CONFIGURATIONS

Will often give the four quantum numbers as __, __, __, __ where the first blank is for the principle quantum number, second blank for the section quantum number, third blank for the magnetic or third quantum number and the last blank for the spin quantum number. Thus the set $2,1,0,-\frac{1}{2}$ describes a 2p electron.

We will use two types of electronic configuration diagrams or notations to describe the electrons present in various elements.

Following is an easy way to memorize the order of electron types **after** the electrons are added. Notice for $n = 1$ there is one type of orbital, the "s" orbital which is one subshell. For $n = 2$ there are two types of orbitals or two subshells, the s and the p. For $n = 3$ there are three types of orbitals or three subshells. The number of types of orbitals is also the number of subshells.

$n = 1$	1s
$n = 2$	2s 2p
$n = 3$	3s 3p 3d
$n = 4$	4s 4p 4d 4f
$n = 5$	5s 5p 5d 5f 5g
$n = 6$	6s 6p 6d 6f 6g 6h
$n = 7$	7s 7p --------------------
$n = 8$	8s ------------------------------

But, electrons are added in another order that is easily remembered by simply taking the diagonals of this same triangle as shown below.

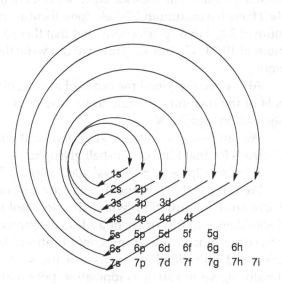

Using the **diagonals** is an easy way to remember the **order of filling** or **addition of electrons** with respect to order subshells have electrons added to them. (This is the order that electrons are added in what is called the Aufbau or Orderly Building Up process.)

And

the order of subshells after filling is simply the horizontal lines. Each horizontal line is a shell with the same principle quantum number.

Each number-letter grouping or combination is a subshell with the same principle quantum number and same secondary quantum number. Thus a 5 d subshell has a n = 5 and "l" = 2. For a 4p we have n = 4 and "l" = 1.

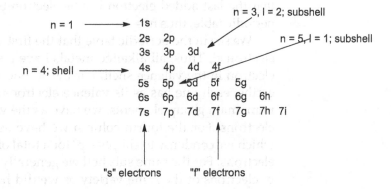

The "order" of filling, or the order to which electrons are added to an atom is found using the diagonals, as noted above, giving the order as 1s>2s>2p>3s>3p>4s>3d>4p>5s>4d>5p>6s> 4f>5d>6p>7s>5f ....

We know that each orbital can have one or two electrons. We also know that within each subshell, each "l" value, within an atom that there is a maximum of two electrons within each orbital so that we can calculate the maximum number of electrons within a subshell by simply multiplying the number of orbitals within that type of subshell by two to give the maximum number of electrons within that subshell type. Since there is one "s" orbital within each shell there is a maximum 2 "s" electons; there are three "p" orbitals with a maximum of 3×2 or 6 "p" electrons; and that there are 5 "d" orbitals with a maximum of 10 "d" electrons ... Thus, we can write the electronic notations for any atom.

Above we described the order of adding electrons by taking the diagonals of the quantum triangle to be 1s>2s>2p>3s>3p>4s>3d>4p>5s>4d>5p >6s> 4f>5d>6p>7s>5f ....

We can now associate the kind of orbital with the **maximum** number of electrons for that kind of subshell giving us

$1s^2 >2s^2 > 2p^6 > 3s^2 >3p^6 >4s^2 >3d^{10} >4p^6 >5s^2 >4d^{10} >5p^6 >6s^2 > 4f^{14} > ....$

We can use this to write the electronic structure for most of the atoms. There are a few situations where this does not follow. For the most part the disobedience to this order of adding electrons is the result of an observation concerning the electronic configurations. In general, nature favors half filled and fully filled subshells. For the s and p subshells we see this in measuring values such as ionization potentials but by the time we get to the d orbitals this tendency is so powerful as to cause a variation to this filling order.

Let us practice creating the electronic configurations for some elements.

Sodium Na, has 11 total electrons. We can use the ordering given above until we get to 11 electrons giving us

$$Na = 1s^2 \, 2s^2 \, 2p^6 \, 3s^1$$

The total number of electrons for Na is 11. The number of total electrons is simply the sum of the superscripts or $2 + 2 + 6 + 1 = 11$.

We believe this is correct because not only do we have our needed eleven electrons but also because of the position that Na has in the periodic table we expect the last added electron to be a "s" electron. If fact, we expect that the last added electron is a 3s electron because Na is in row 3 in the periodic table, thus n = 3.

We see in the periodic table that the first vertical column has as its last electron s^1; Thus, all alkaline metals have a s^1 valence shell with a single electron in the valence shell. For the second vertical column, the alkaline earths, each one has as its valence electrons s^2. For the third vertical column, main group elements, we have as the valence electrons s^2p^1 or three electrons. For the fourth column we have as the valence electrons $s^2p^1p^1$ which we condense to simply s^2p^2 for a total of four electrons as the valence electrons. For the same subshell we generally simply add the total number of electrons of the same variety as we did here. For the fifth vertical column we have as the valence electrons s^2p^3. For the sixth vertical column we have six valence electrons s^2p^4. For the seventh vertical column we have the halogens with 7 valence electrons that are designated as s^2p^5. Finally, we have the eighth vertical column, the rare or nobel gasses, we have eight valence or outer electrons.

Electrons are removed giving cations. The electrons are removed so that the first electrons to be removed have the highest n values and then those with the same n value the highest "l" value. For the main group elements this amounts to the last added, first removed. Sodium typically loses one electron to become Na^{+1} or simply Na^+. The loss of one electron gives the sodium cation or $Na^+ = 1s^2\, 2s^2\, 2p^6$ which is simply a "Ne core" with 10 electrons. Na^+ and Ne are said to be **isoelectronic** meaning they have the same number of electrons-but NOT protons so they remain different elements.

The electronic configuration for fluorine, F, is

$$F = 1s^2\, 2s^2\, 2p^5$$

The total number of electrons for F is 9, that is $2 + 2 + 5$.

Fluorine generally gains a single electron when it forms compounds giving the total number of electrons as 10. This electronic configuration is

$$F^- = 1s^2\, 2s^2\, 2p^6$$

Or simply the "Ne core" and it is also isoelectronic with Na^+ and Ne.

ORBITAL DIAGRAMS

The second type of electronic diagram employs a group of circles, boxes or simple slots with each circle, slot or box representing an **orbital** (with a specific n,l & m quantum number set) and each grouping is a **subshell** (with a specific n & l quantum number combination).

Electrons are designated as arrows, with the particular spin noted by the direction of the arrow. Within a single orbital, if there are two electrons, one arrow must be pointed up and one down showing that the electrons have different spins.

Li $1s^2 2s^1$	↑			
Be $1s^2 2s^2$	↑↓			
B $1s^2 2s^2 2p^1$	↑↓	↑	_	_
C $1s^2 2s^2 2p^2$	↑↓	↑	↑	_
N $1s^2 2s^2 2p^3$	↑↓	↑	↑	↑
O $1s^2 2s^2 2p^4$	↑↓	↑↓	↑	↑
F $1s^2 2s^2 2p^5$	↑↓	↑↓	↑↓	↑
Ne $1s^2 2s^2 2p^6$	↑↓	↑↓	↑↓	↑↓

We have pictured the orbital diagrams for elements 3 through 10, that is, lithium through neon. Notice that each orbital becomes filled with only one electron, half filled, before the second electron is added giving a fully filled orbital. Half filled orbitals gives us unpaired electrons. Thus, lithium has one half filled orbital and one unpaired electron. The number of half filled orbitals is also the number of unpaired electrons. According to Hund's Rule of Maximum Multiplicity, generally simply referred to as Hund's Rule, electrons are added within a subshell giving the greatest number of unpaired electrons, greatest number of half filled orbitals (the same thing) before a second electron is added to "pair" or couple electrons within the same orbital. Thus, the second electron added to the p subshell for carbon is added to a different orbital giving two unpaired electrons or two half filled p orbitals. The next electron giving nitrogen is added to a different orbital giving three half filled orbitals or three unpaired electrons. The p set of orbitals for nitrogen is said to be half filled. The next electron giving oxygen must now couple with an existing electron within the same subshell giving only two unpaired electrons or two half filled orbitals. Finally, for neon, we have all of the orbitals filled giving a fully filled subshell. Such fully filled subshells have an added stability so that rare or nobel gasses form few compounds.

We can set up a number of orbitals corresponding to the order that electrons are added as follows.

1s	2s	2p	3s	3p
—	—	— — —	—	— — —

4s		3d	4p	5s
—		— — — — —	— — —	—

4d

— — — — —

We will now begin adding electrons for the first few element showing both the electronic configuration and orbital diagram for each element.

1s	2s	2p	3s	3p
—	—	— — —	—	— — —

HYDROGEN
 HELIUM

  LITHIUM
   BERYLLIUM

    BORON
     CARBON
      NITROGEN
       OXYGEN
        FLUORINE
         NEON
          SODIUM
           MAGNESIUM

            ALUMINUM
             SILICON
              PHOSPHORUS
               SULFUR
                CHLORINE
                 ARGON

4s	3d	4p
—	— — — — —	— — —

POTASSIUM
CALCIUM
SCANDIUM
TITANIUM
VANADIUM
CHROMIUM-exception-steals 4s electron, adds it to 3d
MANGANESE
IRON
COBALT
NICKEL
COPPER-exception as Cr-steals 4s, adds to 3d
ZINC
GALLIUM
GERMANIUM
ARSENIC
SELENIUM
BROMINE
KRYPTON

PERIODIC TRENDS

Just as there are periodic trends with respect to reactivity and the compounds that are formed, there are other related trends that are actually responsible for the reactivity trends. These trends are all the **inverse** of atomic size or atomic radius. For any given period, the atomic size decreases as we go from left to right. Thus, for the third period we have in order of decreasing size

$$Na> Mg> Al> Si> P> S> Cl> Ar$$

This trend is true for all of the periods.

Next, as we move from top to bottom in any family the atomic size increases. Thus, Be< Mg< Ca< Sr< Ba< Ra so that the bottom of the family is the largest.

The other periodic trends are all inverse of size. Thus, the smaller an atom the

Greater its ionization potential
Generally the greater its electron affinity and
Greater its electronegativity.
And the larger the atom the
Smaller its ionization potential
Generally the smaller its electron affinity and
Smaller its electronegativity.

The **ionization potential** is a measure of the ability of an atom to hold on to its electrons, namely its outer electrons. The ionization potential is defined as

$$A_{(g)} + Energy \rightarrow A_{(g)}^{+1} + e^-$$

The **ionization potential** is the energy required to remove the electron from the atom in its gaseous state. It is an experimentally determined value.

The electronegativity is a scale composed by Linus Pauling to measure the ability of atoms in bonding relationship to attract the shared electrons that form the connective bonding between them. Fluorine was given an electronegativity, EN, value of 4 which is the greatest EN value. Relatively small atoms have generally large EN values. Counter, relatively large atoms such as cesium have small EN values on the order of 0.7. When two atoms form a bond, such as in carbon tetrachloride, there are four C-Cl bonds. The EN of Cl is greater than that of C so that each C-Cl bond is polar with the Cl being partially negative, since it holds more of the electron density; while the carbon is partially positive because its electron density is somewhat given to Cl so it is electron deficient. As we will see, because carbon tetrachloride is symmetrical the net effect is that it does not possess a net dipole.

GRAPHS

Information is given to us in many forms. One of these is in graphs.

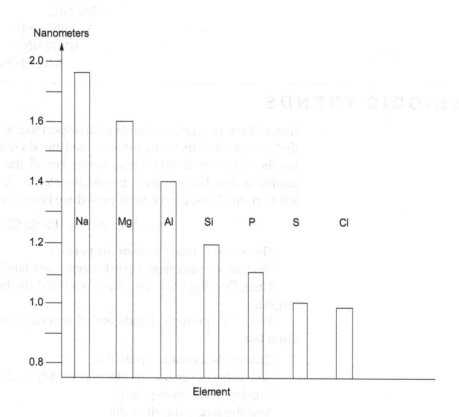

Graph. Atomic diameter as a function of element for the third period elements.

We should be able to draw conclusions from data presented in graph form. First, is there a relationship between the atomic diameter and position of the element in the periodic chart? Second, what is this relationship? To answer this we need to have available to us a periodic chart. After examining the chart we notice that as we move from the extreme left side of the third period to the right the atomic size decreases. This is an important observation and one that will play a role in later discussions.

Let us examine one such relationship that will help us later. This relationship has to do with electronegativity, a measure of the tendency for an atom to attract electron density in a bond.

The relationship between the same elements plotted for size and element above can be graphed showing the electronegativity value for each element.

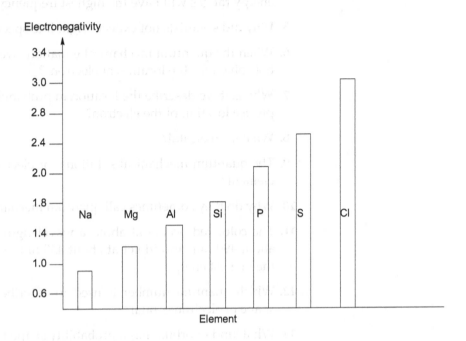

Graph. Relationship between elements of the third period and electronegativity.

First, what is the relationship between the position in the periodic table and electronegativity? Again, looking at the periodic table for the third period we see that the smallest values are for the elements that are to the left and that as we move towards the right in the row the electronegativity values increase.

Finally, is there a relationship between electronegativity and size? To answer this we need to look at both graphs. We see that as the size increases the electronegativity decreases. This is called an inverse relationship. In inverse relationships, as one value increases the other decreases; conversely, as one value decreases, the other value increases. Thus, the relationships are inverse to one another.

Let us see if we can reason why this relationship between size and electronegativity is reasonable.

In science, as in other areas we study, information is given to us in many forms including equations, tables, and graphs. We need to be able to interrupt data when given to us in each of these forms.

PROBLEMS

$E = h\nu$ and $\nu = c/\lambda$ and substitution gives $E = hc/\lambda$.

1. How are frequency and wavelength related?

2. How are energy and wavelength related?

3. Which of the following has the highest, greatest, energy; light with a frequency of 300 mH, 500 mH, or 700 mH?

4. Gamma energy radiation is of high energy while microwave energy is of low energy and visible light is of moderate energy. Which of these energy ranges will have the highest frequency?

5. Why did scientists not expect bright line spectra to occur?

6. When the quantum mechanical equations were solved, why were they not solved for the location of electrons?

7. Why is it we describe the location in probability terms and not give the precise location of the electron?

8. What is an orbital?

9. The quantum mechanical solutions for electrons were based on which element?

10. Why do they sometimes call quantum mechanics wave mechanics?

11. The color red occurs at about a wavelength of 600 nm, blue-green at about 490 nm, and violet at about 430 nm; which color corresponds to the highest energy.

12. Which quantum number is used to describe the average or probably shape of electron orbital?

13. What kind of orbital has a probability shape that is spherical?

14. What kind of orbital has a probability shape that has two elongated lobes?

15. Within a single shell, how many "d" orbitals are there (maximum) and how many maximum electrons can be in these orbitals?

16. Which family of elements all have a single "s" electron as the last electron added?

17. Which family of elements all have two "s" electrons as the last electrons added?

18. What is the valance electronic configuration for all of the halogen elements?

19. Transition elements generally have ____ electrons as their last electrons added.

20. A single orbital can have how many maximum electrons?

21. How many, maximum, electrons can have n = 2?

22. How many, maximum, electrons can have n = 3?

23. Can a single orbital have more than two electrons?

24. How many "p" electrons (maximum) can be within a single atom?

25. What are the four quantum numbers for the last electron added to Na?

26. What is the electronic configuration for Mg?

27. What is the electronic configuration for Mg^{+2}?

28. For l = 2 what kind of electrons are we talking about?

29. Which element will have as its last electron added 4 s?

30. How many d orbitals are there in a single shell?

31. What is the electronic configuration of Ca?

32. How many unpaired electrons does N have?

33. How many half-filled orbitals does an oxygen atom have?

34. Identify an element that has 2 unpaired electrons.

35. Why do elements in the same family have similar chemical properties?

36. Place the following elements in order of **increasing** electronegativity. Mg, Si, S, Cl, Na.

37. Place the following in **increasing** order of ionization potential. Cs, Rb, Li, K

38. Please the following in order of **increasing** size. Ba, Ca, Be, Sr

39. Place the following in order of **decreasing** size from largest to smallest. Li, O, F, C

40. How many electrons in a single atom can have the same n and l quantum numbers?

41. Why should excessive amounts of gamma and x-rays be avoided?

42. How fast does light travel in meters/second?

43. Give the symbols for all four of the quantum numbers and tell what each is chiefly describing.

44. What values can "n" have?

45. What values can "m_l" have?

46. List the orbitals in order from the closest to the nucleus to the furthest from the nucleus to the 5s orbital.

47. What is Hund's rule?

48. How many 2p electrons does carbon have?

49. What neutral atom has an electron configuration of $1s^2 \, 2s^2 \, 2p^6 \, 3s^1$?

50. Which neutral element has an electronic configuration of [Ne] $3s^2$?

51. How many electrons can have n = 2 and l =2?

52. How many electrons can have n = 3 and l = 2?

53. How many electrons can have n = 4, l=2, and m_l = 1?

54. How many electrons can have n = 3, l=2, m_l= 2 and m_s = 1/2?

55. What single spectral observation was most influential in causing scientists to proclaim that we live in a quantized universe?

56. For the figure drawn below where there are five electron energy levels, how many transitions can an electron in n = 1 take part in from only the n = 1 level? Assume for problems 56 to 60 that we are considering only

absorption of energy to promote an electron(s) to a higher or further away from the nucleus, allowed quantum energy level.

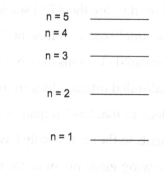

$n = 5$ _____
$n = 4$ _____

$n = 3$ _____

$n = 2$ _____

$n = 1$ _____

Nucleus $+$

57. Of the possible transitions described in problem 56, which transition will have the greatest energy required to make the transition?

58. Of the transitions cited in problem 56, which will correspond to the highest frequency?

59. Of the transitions cited in problem 56, which will correspond to the highest wavelength?

60. Assume that there is a single electron at each of the first four shells, which electron will require the least amount of energy to become promoted or excited to the next energy level?

61. For a single electron residing in $n = 3$, how many spectral lines can be made from the movement of this electron toward the nucleus.

62. When an electron moves from an energy line near the nucleus to one further from the nucleus this is called emission/absorption of energy. Underline the correct term.

63. Give the order that electrons are generally added for the first 10 subshells.

64. Underline the subshells that are not allowed, that is, not possible according to quantum mechanics.

    1s   3p   4s   3d   2d   4f

65. What is the electron configuration for selenium (34)?

66. How many half-filled orbitals and how many unpaired electrons are there for Se?

67. Briefly describe the type of electrons that are being added with respect to the location of elements within the periodic table.

68. What are main group elements?

69. Why do materials such as food heat up readily in a microwave oven while the dish they are in does not?

70. Which energy region causes sun tanning and also skin cancer?

ANSWERS

1. How are frequency and wavelength related?

   According to the relationship $\nu = c/\lambda$ they are inversely related, that is, as one increases the other decreases.

2. How are energy and wavelength related?

   According to the relationship $E = hc/\lambda$ they are inversely related. As the value of one increases the other value decreases. Thus, as energy increases the wavelength decreases; as wavelength increases the energy decreases.

3. Which of the following has the highest, greatest, energy; light with a frequency of 300 mH, 500 mH, or 700 mH?

   According to the relationship $E = h\nu$ energy increases as frequency increases so the greatest energy will be for the highest frequency 700 mH. H is hertz a unit that used to be described in cycles/seconds.

4. Gamma energy radiation is of high energy while microwave energy is of low energy and visible light is of moderate energy. Which of these energy ranges will have the highest frequency?

   According to the relationship $E = h\nu$ energy and frequency are directly related so the highest energy will have the highest frequency so in this case it is the gamma radiation.

5. Why did scientists not expect bright line spectra to occur?

   Scientist expected continuous light spectra but were confused to get the bright line spectra. Eventually the scientists concluded that the universe was quantized and not continuous. This was one of the most unexpected results in science to this time.

6. When the quantum mechanical equations were solved, why were they not solved for the location of electrons?

   Electrons travel at about 1/3 the speed of light so knowing the precise location of an electron means little since the next moment it will be elsewhere. Also, the equations did not allow us to know both the energy and location at the same time.

7. Why is it we describe the location in probability terms and not give the precise location of the electron?

   As noted before electrons travel at about 1/3 the speed of light so knowing the precise location of an electron means little since the next moment it will be elsewhere. Also, the equations did not allow us to know both the energy and location at the same time. Thus, scientists are only able to get an idea of electron location in some probability manner.

8. What is an orbital?

   It is the probability location of an electron.

9. The quantum mechanical solutions for electrons were based on which element?

   The solutions were based on a single electron for the hydrogen atom. But, the results are fairly good for other electrons for other elements.

10. Why do they sometimes call quantum mechanics wave mechanics?

Because the mathematical equations used in quantum mechanics can be used to describe the wave movement as a pebble is dropped into a pool.

11. The color red occurs at about a wavelength of 600 nm, blue-green at about 490 nm, and violet at about 430 nm; which color corresponds to the highest energy.

Again, noting that energy and wavelength are inversely related so the higher the wavelength the lower the energy associated with it. Thus, the highest energy is violet.

12. Which quantum number is used to describe the average or probably shape of electron orbitals?

Second quantum number.

13. What kind of orbital has a probability shape that is spherical?

"s" electrons.

14. What kind of orbital has a probability shape that has two elongated lobes?

"p" electrons

15. Within a single shell, how many "d" orbitals are there (maximum) and how many maximum electrons can be in these orbitals?

Five orbitals maximum times 2 electrons maximum/orbital = 10 maximum electrons.

16. Which family of elements all have a single "s" electron as the last electron added?

Alkaline metals

17. Which family of elements all have two "s" electrons as the last electrons added?

Alkaline earths

18. What is the valance electronic configuration for all of the halogen elements?

s^2p^5

19. Transition elements generally have _____ electrons as their last electrons added.

"d"

Main group elements have as their valence electrons _____ and _____ type electrons with "l"values of _____ and _____.

Filling s and p electrons; that is, they are filling their s and p orbitals. The "l" values are "0" and "1".

20. A single orbital can have how many maximum electrons?

Two.

21. How many, maximum, electrons can have n = 2?

8 electrons.

22. How many, maximum, electrons can have n = 3?

18 electrons-2 s, 6 p, and 10 d.

23. Can a single orbital have more than two electrons?

No. Pauli's law says that all electrons in a single atom must have a different set of quantum numbers and since the m_s spin quantum number can have only two values, you can have only two maximum electrons in a single orbital. The m_s quantum number describes the electrons within a single orbital.

24. How many "p" electrons (maximum) can be within a single atom?

Within a single subshell the answer is 6, but that number varies with the particular element-thus H has no p electrons; Na also has no p electons; Ca has 6 and P has 9, etc.

25. What are the four quantum numbers for the last electron added to Na?

3,0,0 and either + or − ½.

26. What is the electronic configuration for Mg?

$1s^2\ 2s^2\ 2p^6\ 3s^2$ for a total of 12 electrons.

Overall we can use the quantum mechanical triangle to "memorize" the order that electrons are added. This triangle begins

1s				
2s	2p			
3s	3p	3d		
4s	4p	4d	4f	
5s	5p	5d	5f	5g
Etc.				

The order is then is 1s>2s>2p>3s>3p>4s>3d>4p>5s>3d using the diagonals.

27. What is the electronic configuration for Mg^{+2}?

The formal way to do this is to do the electronic configuration for Mg and then remove the two electrons with the highest l value, here it will be the last two electrons added.

$$Mg\ 1s^2\ 2s^2\ 2p^6\ 3s^2 \rightarrow Mg^{+2}\ 1s^2\ 2s^2\ 2p^6$$

28. For l = 2 what kind of electrons are we talking about?

It is good to memorize the values for l with respect to number and kind of orbital.

l	=	0	1	2	3	4	5	...
		s	p	d	f	g	h	...

So for l = 3 we are talking about f orbitals and f electrons and for l = 2 we are considering d orbitals and d electrons.

29. Which element will have as its last electron added 4 s?

The periodic table is arranged according to chemical properties and number of protons, but for neutral elements it is also arranged according to quantum numbers. Thus, transition elements are generally adding d electrons, main group elements are adding s and p electrons. Also, for the row 1 elements, H and He, we have 1s electrons; for row 2 elements are have 2s and 2 p electrons; for the third row elements we are adding

3 s 3 p and for row 4 it is a little more complicated but we are filling 4 s, 4 p and 3 d orbitals. Thus, 4s will be in row four and could be K or Ca.

30. How many d orbitals are there in a single subshell?

5.

31. What is the electronic configuration of Ca?

Ca (20 electrons) we simply use our order of electrons from the triangle and go until we have 20 electrons counting the superscripts which are the electrons.

$1s^2\ 2s^2\ 2p^6\ 3s^2\ 3p^6\ 4s^2$ We get some confidence that this is correct since the last electrons added are s electrons and within the periodic table the elements contained within the two extreme left hand columns are adding s electrons.

32. How many unpaired electrons does N have?

We know that unpaired electrons are derived from having half-filled orbitals. Nitrogen has three p electrons. Since there are three p orbitals that means that each p orbital has one electron in it so there are three total half-filled orbitals and 3 unpaired electrons.

33. How many half-filled orbitals does an oxygen atom have?

Oxygen has for its last added electrons four p electrons added to three p orbitals. Obeying Hund's rule we first half-fill three of the p orbitals and then add the fourth electron to one of the half-filled orbitals leaving now only two half –filled orbitals.

34. Identify an element that has 2 unpaired electrons.

There are many but include O, S, Se, Te, Ti, Zr, C, Si, Ge, Sn.

35. Why do elements in the same family have similar chemical properties?

Chemical properties generally refer to a tendency to react and chemical reactions generally involve gain, loss or sharing of electrons so elements in the same family have the same number of valence electrons.

36. Place the following elements in order of **increasing** electronegativity. Mg, Si, S, Cl, Na.

Na<Mg<Si<S<Cl

The smaller, the greater tendency of an atom in a bond to hold onto electron density.

37. Place the following in **increasing** order of ionization potential. Cs, Rb, Li, K

Cs<Rb<K<Li

The smaller the atom the stronger they will hold onto an electron so higher IP.

38. Please the following in order of **increasing** size. Ba, Ca, Be, Sr

Be<Ca<Sr<Ba

As we go down a given family of elements, size increases.

39. Place the following in order of **decreasing** size from largest to smallest. Li, O, F, C

Li>C>O>F

As we go across a row in the periodic table the elements become smaller.

40. How many electrons in a single atom can have the same n and l quantum numbers?

Depending on what l is they can have 2 for l = 0; 6 for l =1; 10 for l= 2, etc.

41. Why should excessive amounts of gamma and x-rays be avoided?

They are very energetic sufficient to damage our skin and organs.

42. How fast does light travel in meters/second?

3×10^8 m/s

43. Give the symbols for all four of the quantum numbers and tell what each is chiefly describing.

n = general distance of the electrons from the nucleus; shells

l = shapes of orbitals; subshells

m_l = number of orbitals; orbitals

m_s= spin of the electron within a single orbital; single electron

44. What values can "n" have?

n is a small whole number beginning with 1 and as the value increases it designates the electrons are further from the nucleus.

45. What values can m_l have?

m_l can be +/− l including zero. Thus, for l = 2 m_l is 0, +/− 1 and +/− 2. or −2, −1, 0, 1, 2 describing the five d orbitals within a subshell.

46. List the orbitals in order from the closest to the nucleus to the furthest from the nucleus to the 5s orbital.

1s>2s>2p>3s>3p>4s>3d> 4p>5s

47. What is Hund's rule?

Hund's rule says that within a single subshell that the maximum number of half-filled, or unpaired electrons, should be present and that full orbitals should not occur until all the orbitals within the subshell have a single electron in them.

48. How many 2p electrons does carbon have?

It has two 2p electrons.

49. What neutral atom has an electron configuration of $1s^2 2s^2 2p^6 3s^1$?

The compound has 11 electrons and if neutral 11 protons so it is sodium Na.

50. Which neutral element has an electronic configuration of [Ne] $3s^2$?

It is element 12; Mg.

51. How many electrons can have n = 2 and l =2?

None. l has values of n−1 so when n = 2, l can be only 1 and 0.

52. How many electrons can have n = 3 and l = 2?

For l = 2 we have d electrons with 5 orbitals and a maximum of 10 electrons.

53. How many electrons can have n = 4, l = 2, and m_l = 1?

Three quantum numbers designate a single orbital so there can be one or two electrons with the same three quantum numbers.

54. How many electrons can have $n = 3, l=2, m_i = 2$ and $m_s = 1/2$?

Each set of four quantum numbers describes a single electron.

55. What single spectral observation was most influential in causing scientists to proclaim that we live in a quantized universe?

The presence of line spectra rather than continuous spectra.

56. For the figure drawn below where there are five electron energy levels, how many transitions can an electron in $n = 1$ take part in from only the $n = 1$ level? Assume for problems 56 to 60 that we are considering only absorption of energy to promote an electron(s) to a higher or further away from the nucleus, allowed quantum energy level.

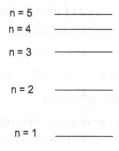

n = 5   ——————

n = 4   ——————

n = 3   ——————

n = 2   ——————

n = 1   ——————

Nucleus   +

Four- $n = 1$ to $n = 2$; $n = 1$ to $n = 3$, $n = 1$ to $n = 4$, and $n = 1$ to $n = 5$.

57. Of the possible transitions described in problem 56, which transition will have the greatest energy required to make the transition?

$n = 1$ to $n = 5$.

58. Of the transitions cited in problem 56, which will correspond to the highest frequency?

Energy is directly proportional to frequency, so the greatest energy and highest frequency transition is the same, $n = 1$ to $n = 5$.

59. Of the transitions cited in problem 56, which will correspond to the highest wavelength?

Energy is inversely proportional to wavelength so it is the transition that requires the least amount of energy, $n = 1$ to $n = 2$.

60. Assume that there is a single electron at each of the first four shells, which electron will require the least amount of energy to become promoted or excited to the next energy level?

Notice that the distance, and therefore energy level difference, between the energy levels diminishes so that the smallest energy gap is between $n = 4$ to $n = 5$.

61. For a single electron residing in $n = 3$, how many spectral lines can be made from the movement of this electron toward the nucleus.

This movement will result in the emission of light. The electron at $n = 3$ can move from $n = 3$ to $n = 2$; $n = 3$ to $n = 1$ and also it can move from $n = 2$ (from a prior movement from $n = 3$ to $n = 2$) to $n = 1$ so three spectral lines can results.

62. When an electron moves from an energy line near the nucleus to one further from the nucleus this is called emission/<u>absorption</u> of energy. Underline the correct term.

63. Give the order that electrons are generally added for the first 10 subshells.

   1s, 2s, 2p, 3s, 3p, 4s, 3d, 4p, 5s, 4d. This is often easily remembered by taking the diagonals of the triangle given before.

64. Underline the subshells that are not allowed, that is, not possible according to quantum mechanics.

   1s   3p   4s   3d   <u>2d</u>   4f

   All are allowed except for the 2d. Again, simply look at the subshell triangle and if the particular subshell is missing, then it is not possible; counter, if it is present, then it is allowed.

65. What is the electron configuration for selenium (34)?

   Again, using the diagonals of the triangle we get

   $1s^2\, 2s^2\, 2p^6\, 3s^3\, 3p^6\, 4s^2\, 3d^{10}\, 4p^4$.

   This is written in the order that the electrons are added. Notice that the superscripts add to 34. The superscripts are the electrons. You might also find this written in the energy level order after electrons are added as follows.

   $1s^2\, 2s^2\, 2p^6\, 3s^3\, 3p^6\, 3d^{10}\, 4s^2\, 4p^4$

66. How many half-filled orbitals and how many unpaired electrons are there for Se?

   Looking at the electronic structure and/or the periodic table we see that there are four p electrons. The electrons are added initially to give only a single electron in each of the three p orbitals. The fourth electron must now couple with one of these half-filled orbitals giving two half-filled and two unpaired electrons. In the periodic table we see that the elements such as

B	C	D	O	F	Ne
p^1	p^2	p^3	p^4	p^5	p^6

   are all filling the p subshell. This is true for all of the elements below them. Thus,

   Al   Si   P   S   Cl   Ar

   are also similarly filling the p subshell. Thus, by observing where an element resides in the periodic we are able to easily predict the number of a type of subshell is being filled and the number of unpaired and half-filled orbitals present.

67. Briefly describe the type of electrons that are being added with respect to the location of elements within the periodic table.

   The furthest to the left two rows, the alkaline metals and alkaline earths are adding s electrons. The next group of element beginning with B through Ne and those directly below them are adding p electrons. The elements that are adding s and p electrons are often called main group elements. The elements between these two groups are called transition elements and they are adding d electrons. The groups below them called the lanthanides and actinides are generally filling their f subshells.

68. What are main group elements?

Main group elements are adding s and p electrons. They appear to the extreme left and right in the periodic table.

69. Why do materials such as food heat up readily in a microwave oven while the dish they are in does not?

Energy in the microwave region corresponds to the energy levels in atoms and molecules that cause the molecules to rotate more rapidly causing friction which creates heat causing materials to heat up, and food to cook. The particular radiation used in the commercial microwaves corresponds to the same energy levels present in water. Thus, materials that contain water heat up readily, while the containers generally are constructed of materials that do not have water in them so do not heat appreciably.

70. Which energy region causes sun tanning and also skin cancer?

Electron movement, and associated breakage of proteins in our skin and formation of pigments in our skin causing our skin to tan, occurs within the ultraviolent region.

SAMPLE TEST PROBLEMS

Name _____ Date _____

Circle only correct answers.

71. How are energy and wavelength related?

a. wavelength = energy;   b. lower the energy, lower the wavelength;
c. higher the energy the lower the wavelength;   d. larger the energy, the higher the frequency;   e. none of the above.

72. Which orbital is described as being spherical?

a. s;   b. p;   c. d;   d. f;   e. none of these.

73. Which of the following correctly describes the arrangement of boron?

a. $1s^2\, 2s^3$;   b. $1s^1\, 2s^1\, 3s^1\, 4s^1\, 5s^1$;   c. $1s^3 2s^2$;   d. $1s^2\, 2s^2\, 2p^1$;
e. none of the above.

74. Sort the following unfilled orbitals by energy, lowest to the highest, that is, the closest to the nucleus to the farthest from the nucleus.

a. 1s, 3s, 5s, 5s, 2,p, 3d;   b. 1s, 2p, 3s, 4s, 3d, 5s;
c. 1s, 2p, 4s, 3s, 3d, 5s;   d. 5s, 3d, 3s, 4s, 2p, 1s;   e. none are correct.

75. Which of the following atoms is the smallest?

a. Cl;   b. At;   c. Br;   d. I;   e. F.

76. In chlorine, Cl, the 3p orbitals have a total of _____ electrons.

a. two,;   b. three;   c. eight;   d. four;   e. five.

77. What needs to be done to convert a neutral oxygen atom into an O^{-2}.

a. remove two protons;   b. add two electrons;   c. add two oxygens;
d. add two protons;   e. remove two electrons.

78. Oxygen, sulfur, and selenium have similar chemical properties because

a. all have the same number of occupied orbitals;   b. all are located close to one another in the periodic table;   c. their outmost p orbitals contain the same number of electrons;   d. these elements do not have similar chemical properties because they are in different periods of the periodic table;   e. they all have similar number of electrons.

79. Which of the following compounds are bonded with ionic bonds?

a. common table salt, NaCl;   b. a sugar, $C_6H_{12}O_6$;   c. water, H_2O;
d. oxygen, O_2;   e. nitrogen, N_2.

80. Why does an electron have both wave and particle properties?

a. it is small and positively charged;   b. it travels about 1/3 the speed of light;   c. it is found in the nucleus;   d. it reacts with protons forming neutrons;   e. it is negatively charged.

81. Which of the following bothered scientists in the early 1900s eventually leading to our view of a quantized world in which we live?

a. microwaves can be dangerous;   b. Einstein's equation $E = mc^2$;
c. bright line spectra rather than continuous spectra were obtained when atoms were bombarded with different kinds of light;

    d. development of Pauli's idea of uncertainty of nuclear energies;

    e. light can be dangerous to our skin causing skin cancer.

82. Titanium has _____ unpaired electrons.

    a. 1;   b. 2;   c. 3;   d. 4;   e. none.

83. Phosphorus has _____ half filled orbitals.

    a. 1;   b. 2;   c. 3;   d. 4;   e. none.

84. A sulfur ion is most likely to have _____ unpaired electrons.

    a. 1;   b. 2;   c. 3;   d. 4;   e. none.

85. Which of the following has the highest number of half filled orbitals?

    a. Cr;   b. C;   c. Na;   d. Li;   e. Sn.

Chemical Structures

BONDING

We talk about secondary and primary bonding. **Secondary bonding** involves associations between different molecules and ions. These associations are not permanent and change with time. Secondary bonding includes hydrogen bonding and is responsible for water being a liquid at room temperature. The various water molecules attract one another and a moment later these water molecules are associated with different water molecules, etc. These associations are said to be momentary. Secondary bonding will not be dealt with here. By comparison, **primary bonds** are more permanent so that the same hydrogen and oxygen atoms are bonded together until some chemical event occurs that causes a breakage and reforming of the oxygen and hydrogen atoms forming new combinations. They are said to be stronger bonds meaning that to overcome the attraction of the bonding atoms more energy is needed. The **bonding energy** is simply the energy needed to break a bond.

$$A-B + Energy \rightarrow A + B$$

It is the primary bonding that forms compounds. We further divide primary bonds into ionic and covalent bonding. Ionic bonding occurs when the members of the bond have quite different tendencies to hold on and attract electrons. Ionic bonds are often formed from reactions between metals and non-metals. Atoms that have lost electrons have a net positive charge and are called **cations** and those that have an excess of electrons have a negative charge and are called **anions**.

Covalent bonds are formed when the bonding pairs have similar tendencies to attract electrons. These are often formed between non-metal atoms. Whenever the bonding atoms are different there is a different tendency towards the shared electrons forming the covalent bond resulting in the atom with greater attracting tendency being having a partially negative charge and the atom having a lesser ability to attract the electrons forming the bond having a partially positive charge. These unlike atoms then form bonds that have **permanent dipoles** and they are said to be **polar bonds.** More about this later.

Here we will focus on the formation of covalent bonds.

Molecular shapes are important in dictating the chemical and physical properties of molecules. Thus, molecular shape is an important consideration in chemistry. In this section we will look at how we can predict the shape of simple molecules from the number of valence electrons present in elements that make up a chemical bond.

Compounds that are largely primarily bonded through covalent bonds have molecular shapes that are dictated by the number of valence electrons. The atoms involved in the formation of covalent bonds are typically non-metals and reside in the right side of the periodic table. We can accurately describe the number of valence electrons by noting which family an element is located in. Looking at a periodic table of the main group elements we can describe the number of valence electrons as follows.

Number of Valence Electrons	1	2	3	4	5	6	7	8
	H							He
	Li	Be	B	C	N	O	F	Ne
	Na	Mg	Al	Si	P	S	Cl	Ar
	K	Ca	Ga	Ge	As	Se	Br	Kr
	Rb	Sr	In	Sn	Sb	Te	I	Xe
	Cs	Ba	Tl	Pb	Bi	Po	At	Rn

Thus, members of a single family all have the same number of valence electrons and will take on the same shape when the same number of bonds are formed. As will be seen compounds of the form H_2X that are members of the same family as oxygen are all tetrahedral/bent for the oxygen family as H_2O, H_2S, H_2Se, H_2Te, and H_2Po.

Before we begin looking at the formation of Lewis structures we will consider some definitions.

BOND LENGTH is the distance between nuclei.

$$A\text{———————}B$$

BOND ORDER is the number of shared electron PAIRS present in the bond. We can have **SINGLE** bonds (one sigma-bond),

$$A\text{—}B$$

DOUBLE bonds (one sigma and one pi-bond), and

$$A=B$$

TRIPLE bonds (one sigma and two pi-bonds).

LEWIS STRUCTURES

We generally draw Lewis structures as part of our journey towards developing the overall geometry of molecules.

LEWIS STRUCTURES or **ELECTRON-DOT formula** focus on the number of bonding or valence or outer-most electrons in an atom. Here a "." represents an electron and ".." Or a "-" represents two electrons. When these electrons are shared between two atoms ".." Or "-" they represents a bond. When the "." or "-" is not involved in bonding they are referred to as **unbonded electrons** or an **unbonded electron pair.** We can draw Lewis structures for both ionic and covalent compounds. Below are Lewis structures for two ionic compounds, NaCl and MgF_2.

$$Na + Cl \rightarrow Na^+ + Cl^- \rightarrow NaCl$$

$$F + Mg + F \rightarrow F^- + Mg^{+2} + F^- \text{ or } Mg + 2F \rightarrow MgF_2$$

It is more common to draw Lewis structures for covalent compounds and from them deduce the structural geometry of the central atom. Following are Lewis structures for some simple covalent bonded compounds.

$$H° + H° \rightarrow H\text{-}H \rightarrow H_2$$

$$H° + Cl° \rightarrow H\text{-}Cl$$

$$H_2 + Cl_2 \rightarrow 2HCl$$

For methane, CH_4 we have

$$
\begin{array}{ccc}
& & \text{H} \\
& & | \\
\text{H·}\overset{..}{\underset{..}{\text{C}}}\text{·H} \longrightarrow & & \text{H-C-H or } CH_4 \\
\text{H} & & | \\
& & \text{H}
\end{array}
$$

For ammonia, NH_3, we have as a Lewis structure the following.

$$
\begin{array}{ccc}
\text{H·}\overset{..}{\text{N}}\text{·H} \longrightarrow & & \text{H-}\overset{..}{\text{N}}\text{-H} \\
\text{H} & & | \\
& & \text{H}
\end{array}
$$

Ammonia has three bonded electron pairs, each pair connecting nitrogen to one of the hydrogen atoms. Each of these bonds is a sigma bond. It also has one unbonded electron pair. Together, it has four sets of electrons or 8 total electrons about nitrogen.

For water, H_2O, we have as a Lewis structure the following.

$$
\begin{array}{ccc}
\text{H·}\overset{..}{\text{O}}\text{·} \longrightarrow & & \text{H-}\overline{\underline{\text{O}}}\text{I} \\
\text{H} & & | \\
& & \text{H}
\end{array}
$$

Water has two bonded electron pairs, each pair connecting the oxygen atom to one of the hydrogen atoms. Each of these bonds is a sigma bond. It also has two unbonded electron pairs. Together, it has four sets of electrons or 8 total electrons about oxygen.

The **octet rule** says that an atom can have no more than eight (valence) electrons about it. In point of fact, only the elements in the second period follow this rule. Why? It is because the second period of elements has only 2s and 2p electrons and can accommodate only a total of eight electrons in its outer shell. By comparison, the third, fourth, etc. periods have shells that also have "d" orbitals and expansion into these "d" orbitals allows the number of outer electrons to be greater than eight.

There are two types of covalent bonds. The first bond formed is a **sigma bond**. For sigma bonds the electron density of the bond is on the bonding axis. The bonding axis is simply a line drawn between the nuclei of the two bonding atoms.

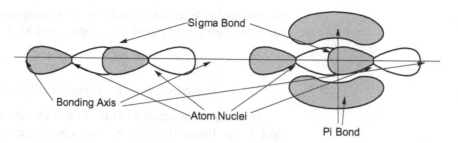

The **pi bond** is the name given to any additional bonds after the formation of the sigma bond. Pi bonds have the electron density about but not on the bonding axis. This is because pi bonds are often formed from the overlap of "p" and "d" orbitals that are not pointed towards one another.

In reality, bonds are not only ionic or covalent, but they often contain both types of bonding even though we will attempt to describe the bonding in terms of ionic or covalent.

ELECTRONEGATIVITY

As noted before, even within a covalent bond, unless the atoms are the same, there is a tendency for one atom to attract more than their fair share (more than 50%) of the bonding electron density. These bonds are said to be polar bonds. Thus, the unequal sharing of the bonding electrons creates the polar bonds.

ELECTRONEGATIVITY is a measure of the ability of an atom in a molecule to attract bonding electrons to itself. Linus Pauling assigned Electronegativity values to atoms constructing a (relative) scale based on "fluorine" being the most electronegative, with an electronegativity, EN, value of 4. In general the EN values decrease from top-to-bottom and increase from left-to-right. In fact, the trend is the same trend found for ionization potentials and is again inverse to size.

Through the use of comparing EN values of two atoms involved in a bond, we can predict if a bond is covalent or ionic and somewhat the extent of covalent character. Further, we can predict which atom in the bonding pair will have an excess of electron density. In general, the closer together two atoms forming the bond the more apt it will be covalent; conversely, to further away from one another, the more apt it is to be ionic.

H							He
Li	Be	B	C	N	O	F	Ne
Na	Mg	Al	Si	P	S	Cl	Ar
K	Ca	Ga	Ge	As	Se	Br	Kr
Rb	Sr	In	Sn	Sb	Te	I	Xe
Cs	Ba	Tl	Pb	Bi	Po	At	Rn

Electronegativity **increases** from left to right in any period (horizontal row) such that the electronegativity increases for the third period Na< Mg<Al<Si<P<S<Cl<Ar. It **decreases** within any family (vertical row) so that O>S>Se>Se and F>Cl>Br>I. In general, the lowest electronegativity values are found in the lower left of the periodic table such as for Cs, Rb, Ba, K and greatest or highest in the upper right corner of the periodic table elements F,

O, Cl. (The rare gasses are generally not included in this approach.) In this arrangement, hydrogen has an electronegativity similar to that of carbon.

The tendency to "want" or attract electrons is generally evaluated using the electronegativities of the two bonded atoms. Thus, for the combination H-H both want electrons the same, since they are the same atom, so that the electron density between them is equally shared and the net electron density is between the two hydrogen nuclei and the bond is said to be **nonpolar** and it does not have a **permanent dipole**.

Now let us consider NaCl. While both Na and Cl want electrons because of the attraction of the positively (has positively charged protons) charged nuclei towards the negativity (electrons have a negative charge) charged electrons. But, the ability to attract electron density is greater for the Cl in comparison to Na so that Cl will attract more of the electron density for the bond. In fact, this difference in ability to attract electron density is so great that Cl takes the electron from Na leaving Cl with one additional electron and a negative charge (Cl^{-1}) and Na one less electron and a positive charge (Na^{+1}). Thus, this great difference in ability or tendency to attract electrons or electron density leads to the formation of **ionic bonds**.

In looking at the bonding for water, H_2O, the tendency for attracting electron density is greater for oxygen compared to hydrogen but it is not so great as to allow electron transfer. Thus, there is an unequal sharing of electrons between the oxygen and hydrogen atom favoring oxygen. Oxygen has a partially negative charge recognizing the greater electron density on the oxygen, and the hydrogen atoms have partially positive charges signifying that the hydrogen atoms have yielded, given, some of the bonded electron charge to the oxygen atom. This unequal sharing of the bonded electrons results in the H-O bond being polar with a net dipole moment. Further, the bonding is still **covalent** since both still share, though unequally, the electron pair.

ELECTRON PAIR GEOMETRY AND MOLECULAR GEOMETRY

The initial step in determining the geometry of molecules is to draw a Lewis structure of the compound. Following is a simple outline that allows a Lewis Electron Dot Formula to be drawn.

1. Calculate the total number of valence or outer electrons.

2. Write a skeleton structure.

3. Distribute electrons to atoms surrounding the central atom. Use the octet rule when applicable.

4. Distribute remaining electrons as pairs.

We often will replace two electrons, two dots with a "-".

Covalent bonds are directional relying on the space taken by available contributing orbitals.

The **Molecular Geometry** is the (general) **shape** of the molecule considering **only** the atoms whereas the **Electron Pair Geometry** includes **both** the atoms and unbonded electron pairs. **It is important to remember that you must determine the electron pair geometry and the molecular geometry is then determined from considering the electron pair geometry.**

The **Valence-shell Electron-Pair Repulsion**, **VSEPR**, **Model** is a model that correctly predicts the shape of molecules in which atoms and unbonded electron pairs are kept as far away from one another as possible because of the repulsion of the nuclei and electron clouds, but they must be close enough to allow good interaction between the bonding electrons and the nuclei.

The geometry of covalent compounds is dependent on the number of electrons about the central atom. These electrons may be bonded electrons and unbonded electrons (generally unbonded electron pairs). As noted before, we will differentiate between the

- arrangement of pairs of electrons dependent on (**electron pair geometry**) **both** unbonded electrons and bonded atoms and
- **molecular geometry** that considers **only** the arrangement of the atoms.

Some helps.

- Determine which is the CENTRAL atom and which are the SURROUNDING atom or atoms.
- Write the electron dot formula concentrating on the number of electron pairs about the central atom.
- Determine the number of "BONDED" and "UN-BONDED" electron pairs about the CENTRAL atom. For pi bonds consider only the sigma bond in the calculation of electron pairs. Each of these **bonded** and **unbonded pairs** will act as "place holders" determining the overall geometry about the **central** atom.

The **Valence-shell Electron-Pair Repulsion**, **VSEPR**, **Model** says that repulsions among bonding or non-bonding electrons of an atom control the angles between bonds from that atom to other atoms surrounding it. The VSEPR theory applies to molecules or covalently bonded compounds but not ionic compounds. As already noted, the VSERP model for molecular geometry is an approach whereby the objects-unbonded electrons (usually pairs) and other atoms connected through bonding- are arranged about the central atom in such a manner as to minimize repulsions due to the like charged electron clouds but maximize the sharing of electron pairs between the positively charged nuclei of the two bonding atoms.

Bonds are normally formed through the sharing of a pair, that is two, electrons. The bonding occurs because of the overlap of the bonding orbitals allowing the bonding electrons to be attracted to the nuclei of the two bonding atoms.

It turns out that most molecules have some symmetry in them and so we use a procedure where hybrid orbitals, equivalent bond sites are formed. Only valence electrons are involved in this hybrid formation. The "names" for these hybrid structures are given in terms of the orbitals that form these structures. Thus, for boron trichloride which is triangular planer, three orbitals on the boron atom are involved with the structure on the boron atom. Originally, boron had an electron description of $1s^2 2s^2 2p^1$ with only the valence or outer electrons, $2s^2 2p^1$, involved. Three half-filled orbitals are needed with each half-filled orbital accepting one electron from Cl. Also, we find experimentally that all Cls are symmetrically arranged about the B. We approach this hybridization knowing that the electrons are arranged with one electron in each of three orbitals, $2s^1 2p^1 2p^1$, and that these three orbitals are hybridized forming three equivalent orbitals with each hybridized orbital having a character based on the original orbitals they were created from, in this case one s orbital and two p orbitals. This arrangement is referred to as a sp^2 hybrid arrangement. BCl_3 has three of these sp^2 hybrid orbitals.

An easy way to remember the name of the hybrid orbital arrangements is to simply remember that each position about the central atom must be equivalent and is hybridized with this in mind. Thus, BCl_3, is a AB_3 arrangement so three orbitals must be involved-one s and two p orbitals so all AB_3 arrangements are sp^2. PF_5 is in the AB_5 grouping so it needs five orbitals, one s three p and two d orbitals so the hybridization is sp^3d^2. The oxygen atom in water is in the group of compounds AB_4 so four orbitals are hybridized, one s and three p orbitals so each of the four orbitals about oxygen is referred to as a sp^3 orbital.

Table 10.1 *Summary of geometrical arrangement based on electron-pair arrangements.*

Positions Central/AB	Electron-Pair Geometry	Molecular Geometry	Example(s)/ Polar-Nonpolar	Hybridization & Bond angle(s)
$2/AB_2$	Linear	Linear*	CO_2, $BeCl_2$/ NP	sp; 180
$3/AB_3$	Triangular Planer	Triangular Planer*	BF_3, H_2CO/ NP	sp^2; 120
$3/AB_3$	Triangular Planer	Bent*	$GeBr_2$, $SnCl_2$/P	sp^2;120
$4/AB_4$	Tetrahedral	Tetrahedral	CCl_4, $SnBr_4$, NH_4^{+1}/NP	sp^3; 109
$4/AB_4$	Tetrahedral	Triangular Pyramidal	NH_3, PCl_3/P	sp^3; 109
$4/AB_4$	Tetrahedral	Bent*	H_2O/P	sp^3; 109
$5/AB_5$	Trigangular Bipyramidal	Triangular Bipyramidal	PCl_5, SnF_5^{-1}/ NP	sp^3d; 90,120,180
$5/AB_5$	Trig. Bipy.	See-saw	SBr_4, SeF_4/P	sp^3d; 90,120,180
$5/AB_5$	Trig. Bipy.	"T"*	IBr_3, $SbCl_3^{-2}$/P	sp^3d; 90,180
$5/AB_5$	Trig. Bipy	Linear*	XeI_2, ICl_2^{-1}/ NP	sp^3d; 180
$6/AB_6$	Octahedral	Octahedral	SCl_6, SeF_6, PF_6^{-1}/NP	sp^3d^2; 90,180
$6/AB_6$	Octahedral	Square Pyramid	$BrCl_5$/P	sp^3d^2; 90,180
$6/AB_6$	Octahedral	Square Planer*	$XeBr_4$/NP	sp^3d^2; 90,180

NP = nonpolar; P = polar; "*" = Planar or flat

When there are NO unbonded electron pairs, the electron pair geometry and molecular geometry are the same. Also, when there are no unbonded electron pairs, the molecules are non-polar. But, when there are unbonded electron pairs present, then the electron pair geometry and molecular geometry are different.

One of the best approaches to having competence with molecular geometry is to memorize Table 1 and to arrange it according to the AB

groupings. Also, you can make inexpensive models using toothpicks and mini-marshmallows.

We refer to unbonded electron pairs using several terms including **unbonded electron pairs** and **lone pairs**. Thus, we will see that water has two lone pairs or unbonded electron pairs on the oxygen while the carbon in methane has no unbonded electron pairs or lone pairs of electrons.

Again, the electron pair geometry involves both unbonded electron pairs and atoms and the molecular geometry involves only atoms- but the electron pair geometry "drives" the molecular geometry. Following are some examples where the geometries are determined though Lewis structures. Here, we will be more formal using the available orbitals about the central atom to govern the geometry about this central aotm.

BeF_2 *Establish the central atom-Be-surrounded by two F.
(We can, at this point also generate the electron-dot arrangement and determine that the compound is <u>LINEAR</u>)

$$F-Be-F$$

*Write the electron configuration for each-Be and F.

$$Be \qquad 1s^2 \qquad 2s^2$$

$$F \qquad 1s^2 \qquad 2s^2 \qquad 2p^5$$

We need to create two <u>half-filled</u> orbitals on Be to overlap with the two (one each) <u>half-filled</u> orbitals on F. To do this, we <u>promote</u> or move forward one of the 2s electrons on Be to one of the 2p (unfilled) orbitals.

This gives us TWO HALF-FILLED orbitals on the Be-one half-filled 2s and one half-filled 2p orbitals.

(We will look ot ONLY the valence or outer electrons)

$$Be \qquad 2s^1 \qquad 2p^1$$

*Since these orbitals will be the same, we <u>HYBRIDIZE</u> THE TWO ORBITALS TO GIVE <u>TWO EQUIVALENT</u> sp ORBITALS-thus two objects surrounding a third-linear. The two "F" positions are the same with a F-Be-F bond angle of 180 degrees.

$$Be \qquad 2sp \qquad 2sp \qquad or \quad TWO\ 2sp\ orbitals$$

$$TWO\ F\ 2s^2 \qquad 2p^5$$

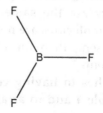

BF_3 -Boron Trifluoride
*Establish the central atom-B surrounded by three F.

(The electron-dot arrangement will have 12 electron pairs-3.5 from each F and 1.5 from B. Thus, we have three "place holders"-the F's-surrounding the B giving a trigonal planer geometry.

*Write the electron configuration for each B and F

B   2s²   2p¹

F   2s²   2p⁵

We need to <u>create</u> THREE <u>half-filled</u> on B to overlap with the three (one each) half-orbitals on F. We do this by <u>promoting</u> or moving forward one of the 2s electrons on B to one of the UNFILLED 2p orbitals giving THREE half-filled orbitals.

B   2s¹   2p¹   2p¹

*Since these orbitals will be the same, we <u>hybridize</u> the THREE orbitals on B giving <u>THREE EQUIVALENT</u> sp² ORBITALS-thus three objects surrounding a fourth-trigonal planer. All bond angles and positions are the same. All F-B-F bond angles are 120 degrees.

B Three 2sp² orbitals

Methane-CH₄
*The central atom is C surrounded by four H. The electron-dot arrangement is <u>TETRAHEDRAL</u>.

*Write the electron configuration for each-C and H

C   2s²   2p²

H   1s¹

We need to <u>create</u> FOUR <u>half-filled</u> orbitals on C to overlap with the FOUR (one each) half-filled 1s orbitals on H. We <u>promote</u> ONE of the 2s electrons into the <u>UNFILLED 2p orbital</u> of C. This will give us FOUR half-filled orbitals on C.

C   2s¹   2p 2p 2p

*To make these orbitals equivalent, we HYBRIDIZE the <u>FOUR</u> orbitals giving <u>FOUR EQUIVALENT</u> sp³ <u>ORBITALS</u>-thus-four objects about a fifth or a tetrahedral geometry. All H-C-H bond angles are about 109.5 degrees.

C Four 2sp³

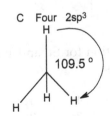

PCl₅

*The central atom is P surrounded by FIVE Cl atoms. The electron-dot arrangement is <u>TRIGONAL BIPYRAMIDAL</u>.

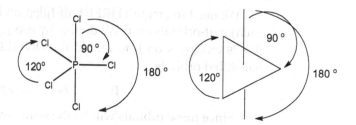

This has two equivalent environments-two "axial" and three planar. The bond angles are 120 for the planar Cl-P-Cl and 180 for the axial Cl-P-Cl

The electron configuration for P and Cl is as follows-outer electrons only

$$P \qquad 3s^2 \qquad 3p^3 \qquad 3d^0$$

$$Cl \qquad 3s^2 \qquad 3p^5$$

We need to <u>create FIVE half-filled</u> orbitals on P to overlap with FIVE (one half-filled each for five Cl's) half-filled orbitals on Cl. We do this through <u>promoting ONE 3s AND ONE 3p (ONE COUPLED 3p PAIR) ELECTRONS-ONE TO AN UNFILLED 3p ORBITAL AND ONE TO A 3d ORBITAL.</u>(Let us now concern ourselves with only the valence or bonding electrons.)

$$P \qquad 3s^1 \qquad 3p^1 \qquad 3p^1 \qquad 3p^1 \qquad 3d^1$$

*Since these orbitals are the same, we <u>hybridize</u> the five orbitals on P giving <u>FIVE EQUIVALENT</u> sp³d orbitals.

$$P \qquad Five \qquad 3sp^3d \quad orbitals$$

SeF₆

*The central atom is Se surrounded by SIX F atoms. The electron-dot arrangement is that of an <u>OCTAHEDRAL</u>-all SIX "F" positions are equivalent-the same. Bonding angle 90 degrees for F-Se-F.

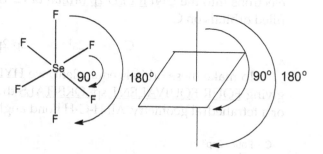

*The electron configuration for Se and F is as follows-giving only the valence or bonding electrons.

$$Se \qquad 4s^2 \qquad 4p^4 \qquad 4d^0$$
$$F \qquad 2s^2 \qquad 2p^5$$

We need to <u>create</u> <u>SIX half-filled orbitals</u> on Se. We do this by moving ONE 4s and TWO 4p electrons-ONE WILL GO TO AN UNFILLED 4p ORBITAL AND TWO WILL GO TO UNFILLED 4d orbitals.

$$Se \quad 4s^1 \quad 4p^14p^14p^1 \quad 4d^14d^1$$

*Since these SIX orbitals are the same, we <u>HYBRIDIZE</u> the SIX orbitals on Se giving <u>SIX EQUIVALENT</u> sp^3d^2 orbitals.

$$Se \quad Six \ 4sp^3d^2 \quad orbitals$$

The **dipole moment** is a measure of the degree of charge separation in a molecule. The greater the DIPOLE MOMENT, typically the greater the IONIC character of the bond. For **SYMMETRICAL** molecules where the DIPOLE MOMENTS cancel one another, the DIPOLE MOMENT is zero, even though the particular bonds can be polar. Thus, there is a relationship between a molecules DIPOLE MOMENT and its MOLECULAR GEOMETRY.

Following are examples where there are polar bonds but where the **entire** molecule is **non-polar**, does **not** have a permanent dipole or dipole moment.

$$CF_4 \quad O=C=O \quad BBr_3$$

Following are examples where the molecules **contain** polar bonds and where the entire molecule **is** polar and has a permanent dipole or dipole moment.

$$CO \quad CHCl_3 \quad BBr_2Cl$$

The five basic electron pair geometries are given below.

MULTIPLE BONDING

In some cases, there may be more than one bond between the same two atoms.

The initial or first bond is **always** a <u>SIGMA</u> bond where the <u>electron density lays **ON** the bonding axis.</u> **Subsequent** bonds are <u>Pi</u> bonds where the <u>electron density lays **ABOUT** the bonding axis.</u>

Let us look at several examples.

$$ETHYLENE, \ CH_2=CH_2$$

We will treat ethylene as though it has <u>TWO CARBONS that are CEN-TRAL ATOMS</u>. Here, each carbon is surrounded by two hydrogens and one carbon. Thus, the geometry arrangement about each carbon is the SAME and it is <u>TRIGONAL PLANAR</u>. We then need <u>THREE HALF-FILLED ORBITALS ON **EACH** THE CARBON</u>. We get these by promotion of <u>ONE 2s ELECTRON TO A VACATE 2p ORBITAL.</u>

$$C \quad 2s^2 \quad 2p^2$$

$$C \quad 2s^1 \quad 2p^1 \, 2p^1 \, 2p^1$$

This creates <u>FOUR half-filled</u> orbitals of which only <u>THREE</u> will be used to form <u>THREE SIGMA</u> bonds. These <u>THREE HALF-FILLED ORBITALS will be hybridized forming THREE EQUIVALENT sp^2 orbitals.</u>

The <u>REMAINING HALF-FILLED</u> orbital on C, a p orbital, is at such an orientation that it can only overlap with a similar (left-over) half-filled orbital on the second C <u>ABOUT THE BONDING AXIS FORMING A PI BOND-THE SECOND BOND TO CARBON.</u>

H₂CO, Formaldehyde

*The central atom is the C surrounded by two H's and one O.

Let us focus on two atoms this time-the C and O. The ground state electronic configuration is

$$\begin{array}{ccc} C & 2s^2 & 2p^2 \\ O & 2s^2 & 2p^4 \end{array}$$

The oxygen needs two half-filled orbitals-one will form a sigma bond with carbon and the second will form a pi bond with carbon- and each hydrogen needs one half filled orbital.

We need <u>THREE HALF-FILLED</u> orbitals on carbon-two to overlap, form sigma bonds, with the two hydrogens and one to overlap with the one oxygen. We form these THREE HALF-FILLED orbitals through promotion of the 2s electron to an empty 2p orbital. This generates FOUR <u>NOT</u> THREE HALF-FILLED ORBITALS ON THE CARBON ATOM. We form then three hybridized sp^2 orbitals-that will give us <u>THREE SIGMA</u> BONDS-ONE TO EACH OF THE TWO HYDROGENS AND ONE TO THE SINGLE OXYGEN ATOM.

$$\begin{array}{c} H \\ C{-}O \\ H \end{array}$$

We now focus on both the remaining vacate half-filled 2p orbital on C and on the REMAINING 2p <u>VACATE</u> unfilled orbital on oxygen. <u>These two form a pi bond through the overlapping of the two half-filled 2p orbitals-one on C and one on O.</u>

ACETYLENE

Here, the central atoms are the two carbons. Let us focus on only one of the carbons. We need <u>TWO HALF-FILLED</u> orbitals-one for the H and one for the other C. We get these through promotion of one of the 2s electrons to a vacate 2p orbital of C.

$$C \qquad 2s^2 \qquad 2p^2 \qquad \rightarrow \qquad 2s^1 \qquad 2p\ 2p\ 2p$$

We will now form a hybride of <u>ONE 2s ORBITAL AND ONE 2p</u> orbital. This gives us two sigma bonds-one each to the carbon and the hydrogen.

H —C— C   And for both carbons   H —C—C— H

We now draw our attention to the second C seeing that it, and the first carbon, both HAVE <u>TWO</u> HALF-FILLED orbitals remaining. These two remaining half-filled orbitals can overlap with the two half-filled orbitals of the second carbon forming <u>TWO pi BONDS.</u>

HC≡≡≡≡CH

In general, carbon forms four bonds and oxygen forms two bonds. As noted above, carbon can form these four bonds to four different atoms such as in methane, CH_4, where there are four sigma bonds; or three different atoms with one double bound as in ethylene, $CH_2=CH_2$, where there are three sigma bonds and one pi bond; or two different atoms as in acetylene where there are two sigma bonds and two pi bonds. Oxygen forms two bonds in two ways. First, it can form two sigma bonds to two different atoms as in water, H_2O; or it can form a double bond with one sigma bond and one pi bond as in formaldehyde, $H_2C=O$. One interesting exception to this is carbon monoxide where carbon forms three bonds to oxygen and oxygen forms three bonds to carbon.

C≡O

WATER

As noted before water is a polar molecule. This polarity makes water a liquid at room temperature because it allows the formation of hydrogen bonds between different water molecules. This results in water molecules acting as a group reducing their tendency to enter the vapor state, thus water is a liquid at room temperature.

Liquid water   Solid water

Above are structures of liquid water and solid water with hydrogen bonding locations noted by arrows.

Hydrogen bonding occurs when a hydrogen is attached to a highly electronegative atom such as oxygen, nitrogen, fluorine, and chlorine and this hydrogen is then approached by another highly electronegative atom. Thus, for water, one hydrogen on a water molecule is approached by the oxygen of a second water molecule forming the hydrogen bond.

Because the density of the liquid water is greater than that of the solid, ice floats on liquid water. Essentially all other liquids are less dense than the solid form.

The polar nature of water acts to dissolve many ionic compounds with the partially positive hydrogen portion pointing towards the anion and the partially negative oxygen portion pointing towards the cation. This is illustrated for NaCl, common table salt, below.

PROBLEMS

1. How many valence electrons does sulfur have?

2. How many valence electrons does bromine have?

3. What is the electron pair arrangement for BBr_3?

4. What is the molecular geometry for BBr_3?

5. What is the bond angle present in BBr_3?

6. Is BBr_3 a polar molecule?

7. Is BBr_3 planar?

8. How many unbonded electron pairs are there about carbon in methane, CH_4?

9. What is the electron pair geometry of the bonds and associated hydrogen atoms about carbon in methane, CH_4?

10. What is the bond angle in methane, CH_4?

11. Is methane, CH_4, planar?

12. Is the methane molecule CH_4, polar?

13. What is the electron pair geometry of carbon tetrachloride?

14. Is chloroform, $CHCl_3$ polar?

15. How many unbonded electron pairs are there on the oxygen atom in water?

16. What is the electron pair geometry about the oxygen in water?

17. What is the molecular geometry arrangement about the oxygen atom in water?

18. Is water polar?

19. What is the bond angle in water?

20. What is the electron and molecular geometry of NH_3?

21. Is ammonia polar and planar?

22. What is the electron and molecular geometry of phosphorus trifluoride?

23. What is the electron and molecular geometry of the ammonium ion, NH_4^+?

24. What is the electron pair and molecular geometry of $COCl_2$?

24. For the molecule $COCl_2$ is the molecule planar and/or polar and what are the approximate bond angles?

25. What is the electron pair and molecular geometry for $POCl_3$?

26. Is the molecule $POCl_3$ polar and if so what positions on the molecule are partially negative and partially positive?

27. Would you expect turpentine, a nonpolar solvent, to be miscible (soluble) in water? Why?

28. Is water and ethanol, CH_3CH_2OH, a relatively polar molecule miscible with one another.

29. Would you expect the bonding in calcium oxide to be ionic?

30. Which of the following would you expect to be the most polar bond? C-O; C-S; C-Se

31. Which of the following will be most nonpolar? O=O; C=O; C=S

32. Proteins are composed of amino acids. The general structure of the amino acid alanine is

Give the geometry for each of the three carbon atoms.

33. In question 32, what kind of hybridization does each carbon have.

34. What is the electron pair and molecular geometry for antimony pentachloride?

35. What is the electron pair and molecular geometry for antimony trichloride?

35. A nucleic acid is composed of deoxyribose sugars connected to a phosphate and a nitrogen-containing compound for each repeat unit. Below is one unit containing the phosphate and deoxyribose sugar unit. Describe the geometry present on the phosphorus on the phosphate and for all of the carbon atoms in the sugar.

36. The electron configuration of a neutral atom is $1s^2\ 2s^2\ 2p^6\ 3s^2\ 3p^4$ has _____ valance electrons. Which element is this?

37. Given that the element in 36 reacts bonding with 4 Cl atoms. What would be its electron geometry?

38. How are NCl_3, CF_4, and H_2O similar with respect to their geometry?

39. What is the electron pair and molecular geometry of H_3O^+?

40. Which of the following has the highest electronegativity value? Al, C, F, O.

41. What part do double bonds play in determining the overall structure of a compound?

42. Why is carbon dioxide linear rather than some other electron pair geometry?

43. What is the electron pair geometry of tin tetrabromide?

44. What is the bond angle(s) for tin tetrabromide? Is tin tetrabromide planar?

45. Which bond is the most polar? C-F; C-Cl; C-Br; C-I?

46. For the bonds given in problem 45, which bond is the least polar?

47. Which of the following compounds is ionic? NO; CBr_4; $LiNO_3$; SBr_4

48. Since oxygen generally forms two bonds, what would you expect the bonding in an oxygen molecule to be?

49. There is a saying that atoms cannot have more than eight electrons about them. This is referred to as the octet rule. Many compounds have more than eight electrons about them. How is this possible?

50. Which of the following compounds has more than eight electrons about the central atom? CCl_4; SBr_4; SI_6; CO_2; KI

51. How many electrons are about Xe in $XeBr_6$?

52. Which of the following has the same electron pair geometry as sulfur tetrabromide?

    SeI_4; SCl_4; $AsBr_4^-$; SnI_4^{-2}

53. What is the electron pair geometry for $XeBr_4$?

54. What is the molecular geometry for xenon tetrabromide?

55. Remembering that carbon typically forms four bonds, either to two, three, or four different atoms, predict the structure for ethylene, C_2H_4. Hint, the carbon atoms are bonded to one another.

56. List the following in order of increasing electronegativity. C, B, O, F, Be

57. Which of the following does not contain both an ionic and covalent bond? $Ca(OH)_2$; $LiNO_3$; $BaSO_4$; $SrCO_3$

58. What would you expect to be the formula from the reaction of an aluminum ion and selenium ion?

59. Which of the following has the most unbonded electron pairs about the central atom?

60. For the compound HONO where nitrogen is the central atom, what is the electron pair geometry about nitrogen?

ANSWERS

1. How many valence electrons does sulfur have?

Sulfur has 6 valence electrons. By noting the position in the periodic table we can readily determine the valence electrons of elements here focusing on the main group elements since they are the ones that generally form covalent bonds and covalent compounds that we will emphasize here in our efforts on determining their geometries. Thus, all of the elements in row 3A (13) as B, Al have 3 valance electrons; those in 4A (14) such as C, Si, have 4 valence electrons; those in 5A (15 such as N, P, all have 5 valence electrons; etc.

2. How many valence electrons does bromine have?

Bromine is in row 7A (17) so has 7 valence electrons.

3. What is the electron pair arrangement for BBr_3?

Boron has 3 valence electrons and Br has 7 valence electrons with one half-filled orbital. Thus, each B will have 3 Br surrounding it with no unbonded electrons on the B. It is of the AB_3 general structure, Table 1. The question is how do we arrange three Br about B, the central atom, so that they are as far away from one another, due to the repulsion of the bonded electron pairs, yet retain the attraction to the nuclei of B and Br. The answer is triangular planar.

4. What is the molecular geometry for BBr_3?

From problem 3 we determined that B in BBr_3 has no unbonded electron pairs. In all such cases **where there are no unbonded electron pairs associated with the central atom the electron pair geometry and molecular geometry are the same.**

5. What is the bond angle present in BBr_3?

As noted in problem 3 we have three atoms, Br, surrounding a fourth central atom B so they will form a triangular planar geometry as pictured for problem 3. The bond angle is determined from considering a circle with 360^0 and dividing it into three equal sections, $360/3 = 120$ degrees. Thus, the bond angle is 120 degrees.

6. Is BBr_3 a polar molecule?

BBr_3 is composed of three polar B-Br bonds but because they are symmetrically arranged about B their polarity are negated so the total molecule is not polar and does not have a permanent dipole. We see that **symmetrical molecules are not polar.**

7. Is BBr_3 planar?

Planar is another name for flat. In this case, the very name triangular planar says that it is planar or flat. Thus, it is planar. In some cases you need to figure out a system to determine if a molecule is flat or not, even if it requires memorizing Table 10.1.

8. How many unbonded electron pairs are there about carbon in methane, CH_4?

Carbon has four valence electrons, 2 s electrons and 2 p electrons. Each hydrogen has one half-filled orbital and forms bonds by sharing its half-filled orbital electron with an electron from another atom forming a covalent bond. Since there are 4 electrons in the valence shell of carbon each electron will be shared with one of the hydrogen half-filled orbitals forming four sigma bonds. These bonds are considered to be equal and so are said to be hybridized into four bonds. Since the bonds are formed with one s electron and 3 p electrons each hybridized orbital is said to be a sp^3 orbital. Because all 4 of carbon's electrons are bonded there are no unbonded electron pairs about carbon.

9. What is the electron pair geometry of the bonds and associated hydrogen atoms about carbon in methane, CH_4?

As noted in the problem above, there are four equal arrangements of the hydrogen atoms and associated bonded electrons about carbon. The question is how can four bonded hydrogen atoms be arranged to minimize the electron repulsion (since like charges repeal one another) yet be attracted to the proton rich nuclei of the carbon and hydrogen atoms. The answer is to form a tetrahedral structure.

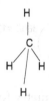

10. What is the bond angle in methane, CH_4?

We will see that most of the bond angles can be calculated by dividing a circle, 360 degrees, into sections, but the tetrahedral bond angle is an exception and we simply need to memorize that it is about 109 degrees. Since the geometry of all four hydrogen atoms is the same, all the bond angles are the same, 109 degrees.

11. Is methane, CH_4, planar?

Methane is not planar.

12. Is the methane molecule, CH_4, polar?

Because it is a symmetrical molecule methane is not polar.

13. What is the electron pair geometry of carbon tetrachloride?

You need to know that carbon tetrachloride is CCl_4. It is in the same geometrical grouping as methane with carbon surrounded by 4 Cl rather than 4 H. Each Cl has one half-filled orbital that "overlaps" with one of the electrons on carbon forming 4 covalent bonds. Thus, carbon tetrachloride has an electron and molecular geometry of tetrahedral.

14. Is chloroform, $CHCl_3$ polar?

Chloroform has the same basic geometry as carbon tetrachloride and methane but is not symmetrical so it is polar. Chloroform has unlike atoms surrounding the carbon, three Cl and one H so it is not completely symmetrical.

Further, because the atoms attached to the central carbon differ, the bond angles will differ but that difference is small so we will call all the bond angles 109 degrees.

15. How many unbonded electron pairs are there on the oxygen atom in water?

Oxygen has 6 valence electrons, 2s and 4p electrons. Two of these electrons overlap with the half-filled orbital of each hydrogen atom forming two primary sigma bonds. The remaining four electrons couple forming two sets of unbonded electrons, two unbonded electron pairs.

16. What is the electron pair geometry about the oxygen in water?

In the problem above we established that there are two bonded electron pairs one each between the oxygen and hydrogen atoms, and two unbonded electron pairs giving a total of 4 electron pairs about the oxygen. These 4 electron pairs are said to be hybridized giving 4 similar geometrical environments. The geometry question is then, how can four electron pairs be arranged to that they are as far away from one another since electrons have the same change and repeal one another, and yet form bonds with the two hydrogen atoms and form the two unbonded electron pairs, be associated with the positive (because of the protons) nucleus of oxygen. The answer is that they form a tetrahedral electron pair geometry.

17. What is the molecular geometry arrangement about the oxygen atom in water?

We differentiate between two geometries. The electron geometry considers both the bonded AND unbonded electron pairs. The molecular geometry considers only the bonded electron bonds, that is only the electron pairs that attach another atom to the central atom. **Whenever there are unbonded electron pairs present on the central atom the electron and molecular geometries will be different**.

Of importance, in order to correctly identify the molecular geometry we must determine first the electron pair geometry or we will wrongly give the molecular geometry. Thus H_2O is often depicted as H-O-H simply because it is easier to type yet we see that is it wrong. This is the geometry we might identify for water if we simply considered bonds to the hydrogen. We see that this assignment is wrong. We see that the true geometry of water is bent, not straight, and that is its molecular geometry is bent.

Also of interest is that the geometries determined using our approach are correct as determined by spectronic techniques that show the true or real geometry of the molecules.

18. Is water polar?

Because the structure for water is not symmetrical, the molecule is polar. In fact, it is this polarity that is responsible for many of the properties of water, that causes water to be a liquid under normal room conditions. This polarity allows the formation of hydrogen-bonding, the critical secondary bonding in water and in most biologically important molecules such as proteins and nucleic acids and allows the solubility of many polar compounds in water.

19. What is the bond angle in water?

We have seen that the arrangement of the two hydrogen atoms and two unbonded electron pairs are in a tetrahedral arrangement. The general bond angle for a tetrahedral arrangement is about 109 degrees. But, because of the added repulsion of the unbonded electron pairs on the oxygen atom, the actual H-O-H bond angle is less than that.

20. What is the electron and molecular geometry of NH_3?

Nitrogen is a 5A (15) element with 5 valence electrons. Each hydrogen has one half-filled orbital. Thus, three of the five electrons about nitrogen will fill the three half-filled orbitals in the three hydrogen atoms. This leaves two unbonded electrons that form an unbonded electron pair. Thus, this is a AB_4 type of molecule so has an electron geometry that is tetrahedral and a molecular geometry that is triangular pyramidal.

21. Is ammonia polar and planar?

Ammonia is polar because it is not symmetrical about nitrogen and it is not planar. The name, triangular pyramidal tells us that it is pyramidal and pyramids are not flat.

22. What is the electron and molecular geometry of phosphorus trifluoride?

First we need to know from the name that phosphorus trifluoride is PF_3. Phosphorus is a 5A (15) element, the same as nitrogen in problem 20 above. It has the same number of atoms about it, three. It also has one unbonded electron pair. Again, this is all similar to ammonia. So it is expected that it will have the same electrical and molecular geometry as ammonia and it does. It has an electron geometry of tetrahedral and molecular geometry that is triangular pyramidal.

23. What is the electron and molecular geometry of the ammonium ion, NH_4^+?

While N is a 5A (15) element having 5 valence electrons, the positive charge is generally handled by removing one of these electrons from the central atom, nitrogen, leaving 4 valence electrons. Each of these four electrons will overlap with one of the half-filled orbitals of the hydrogen atoms. Thus, four sigma bonds are about the central atom nitrogen. This is then of the general form AB_4. Because there are no unbonded electron pairs about the nitrogen, the electron pair and molecular geometries are the same, tetrahedral.

24. What is the electron pair and molecular geometry of $COCl_2$?

Most central atoms want to form multiple bonds. They can do so such that each bond is a single bond or they may do so where multiple bonds occur between two atoms. Carbon and oxygen are two examples that we need to be aware of forming multiple bonds to the same atom. Carbon almost always forms four bonds. And, oxygen almost always forms two bonds. For oxygen, these two bonds, formed from the presence of two half-filled orbitals can be directed at two different atoms such as in the case of water, or to the same atom as in this case with $COCl_2$. We can arrange the atoms about carbon so that two of the electrons overlap with two half-filled orbitals on Cl and two of the carbon electrons overlap with two half-filled orbitals on O. Thus, we have our four bonds for carbon and two bonds for oxygen.

We need to understand that the first bond to an atom is called a sigma bond and only sigma bonds and unbonded electron pairs "count" towards determining the overall geometry about the central atom. The second bond between the oxygen and carbon atoms is called a pi bond and essentially wraps about the sigma bond so it does not force any new geometry. When we designate a double bond we generally simply show two bonds, such as C=O, without designating which of the two lines is the pi and which is the sigma bond.

Thus, we have three objects, one O and two Cls about the carbon $COCl_2$ is a AB_3 molecule. The electron pair and molecular geometry is that of a trigonal planar.

24. For the molecule $COCl_2$ is the molecule planar and/or polar and what are the approximate bond angles?

Since $COCl_2$ is a triangular planar, it is flat and since it is not symmetrical it is polar. The bond angle is approximately 120 degrees.

25. What is the electron pair and molecular geometry for $POCl_3$?

Phosphorus has five valence electrons since it is a 5A (15) element. Three of these electrons with overlap with the three half-filled orbitals on chlorine. The remaining two electrons will overlap with the two half-filled orbitals of oxygen. Thus, we have four objects, three Cls and one O, about the central P, making it a AB_4 molecule meaning it is a tetrahedral electron pair and because there are not unbonded electrons about P it is also the molecular geometry.

26. Is the molecule $POCl_3$ polar and if so what positions on the molecule are partially negative and partially positive?

We have already established that $POCl_3$ is tetrahedral. The electronegativities for O and Cl are greater than for P so the bond densities, amount of electron density, will lay towards the atoms with the higher electronegativites and the atom, P, with the lower electronegativity will have be somewhat electron deficient so it will be electron poor acting as a partially positive site.

27. Would you expect turpentine, a nonpolar solvent, to be miscible (soluble) in water? Why?

Water is relatively very polar whereas turpentine is nonpolar. In solubility, likes generally will dissolve and be miscible with like polar molecules. Counter, solvents and compounds that are unlike in polarity, such as in this case, often are not soluble or miscible with one another. Thus, as expected, turpentine and water are not miscible with one another.

28. Is water and ethanol, CH_3CH_2OH, a relatively polar molecule miscible with one another.

As noted above, molecules with similar polarities are generally miscible while those with unlike polarities are immiscible with one another. Thus, because both are fairly polar so they are probably miscible with one another.

29. Would you expect the bonding in calcium oxide to be ionic?

Yes. Ca has a low electronegativity while O has a relatively high electronegativity so it is probable that O takes electrons from Ca forming ionic bonding between them.

30. Which of the following would you expect to be the most polar bond? C-O; C-S; C-Se

In this series, the carbon remains the same but the other element changes. The electronegativities for the associated elements are O>S>Se so the most polar with be C-O.

31. Which of the following will be most nonpolar? O=O; C=O; C=S

C=O and C=S are mildly polar but O=O is nonpolar so it will be the most nonpolar.

32. Proteins are composed of amino acids. The general structure of the amino acid alanine is

Give the geometry for each of the three carbon atoms.

Carbon 1 is attached to four different atoms, one carbon and three hydrogen atoms so it is a AB_4 tetrahedral arrangement for both the electron pair and molecular geometries. Carbon two is attached to two carbon atoms and one nitrogen atom and one hydrogen atom that is not shown so it is also a tetrahedral geometry. A question is how do we know that about the hydrogen atom that is not shown. In these type of structures hydrogen atoms are often omitted, particularly when attached to a carbon atom. We know that carbon atoms have four bonds and here it has three without the hydrogen so the fourth bond must be with the unshown hydrogen atom. Carbon 3 is attached to a carbon, and two oxygen atoms; one oxygen atom is singly bonded to the OH and one is double bonded to the carbon. Thus, carbon 3 is bonded to three different atoms so it is a AB_2 trigonal planar geometry.

33. In question 32, what kind of hybridization does each carbon have.

In Table 1 we see that we can actually associate the hybridization to the number of bonds formed and number of unbonded electron pairs. Thus, for carbons 1 and 2 the carbon is bonded to four different atoms so it is tetrahedral and sp^3 hybridization. For carbon 3 it is bonded to three different atoms so is a trigonal planar geometry with a sp^2 hybridization.

34. What is the electron pair and molecular geometry for antimony pentachloride?

Antimony pentachloride is $SbCl_5$. Sb is a 5A (15) element so it has 5 electrons. Each of these electrons will bond with a single Cl so we have $SbCl_5$ being AB_5 type of geometry so it is then trigonal bipyrimidal. Since there are no unbonded electron pairs, the electron pair and molecular geometries are the same.

35. What is the electron pair and molecular geometry for antimony trichloride?

Again, antimony has 5 valance electrons. Three of these will overlap with three half-filled orbitals on Cl. Remaining will be a set of electrons that form an unbonded electron pair. Thus, there are four objects, three bonded Cls and one unbonded electron pair, about Sb. So the molecule is of a AB_4 variety and is tetrahedral for the electron pair geometry. The molecular geometry is a trigonal pyramid.

35. A nucleic acid is composed of deoxyribose sugars connected to a phosphate and a nitrogen-containing compound for each repeat unit. Below is one unit containing the phosphate and deoxyribose sugar unit. Describe the geometry present on the phosphorus on the phosphate and for all of the carbon atoms in the sugar.

With the knowledge we have we can describe the geometry of atoms composing even the most complex molecules if we look at them atom-by-atom. The P in the phosphate has 5 valence electrons. Three of these electrons are part of the O-P bond with the phosphorus offering one electron to each of the three oxygen atoms. The last two electrons are shared with the fourth oxygen, P=O. Thus, the phosphorus has four groups surrounding it and is of the grouping AB_4 and is tetrahedral. Each carbon is bonded to four different atoms so each carbon is also of the AB_4 variety and is tetrahedral.

36. The electron configuration of a neutral atom is $1s^2\ 2s^2\ 2p^6\ 3s^2\ 3p^4$ has _____ valence electrons. Which element is this?

This is element 16, S, and it has six valence electrons, two 3s electrons and four 3p electrons.

37. Given that the element in 36 reacts bonding with 4 Cl atoms. What would be its electron geometry?

The element would have 4 bonded electron pairs to the four Cl atoms and two unbonded electrons that would form an unbonded electron pair making the compound a AB_4 variety and a tetrahedral electron pair geometry.

38. How are NCl_3, CF_4, and H_2O similar with respect to their geometry?

All have an electron pair geometry that is tetrahedral.

39. What is the electron pair and molecular geometry of H_3O^+?

Oxygen has 6 valence electrons. The loss of an electron giving the molecule a net "+" is generally assigned to the central atom, here oxygen. Thus, the oxygen in H_3O^+ will be given 5 electrons. Three of these electrons will bond with the half-filled orbitals of the three hydrogen atoms leaving two unbonded electrons that form an unbonded electron pair. Thus H_3O^+ is of the group AB_4 taking on a tetrahedral electron pair structure. The molecular structure is a trigonal pyramidal.

40. Which of the following has the highest electronegativity value? Al, C, F, O.

F was given the highest EN value of 4 by Pauling so it will have the highest EN value.

41. What part do double bonds play in determining the overall structure of a compound?

The second bond between two atoms resides "about" an already existing sigma bond so it does not contribute to the overall structure.

42. Why is carbon dioxide linear rather than some other electron pair geometry?

In general, carbon forms four bonds and oxygen two bonds. In carbon dioxide, there are two bonds formed between the carbon atom and each oxygen, O=C=O, with the second bond in each case a pi bonds formed about an existing sigma bond. Since pi bonds are formed around existing sigma bonds they do not provide additional geometrical locations. Thus, carbon dioxide is an AB_2 type of molecule and is linear.

43. What is the electron pair geometry of tin tetrabromide?

Tin tetrabromide, $SnBr_4$, is a tetrahedral similar to carbon tetrabromide, lead tetrachloride, etc. Tin, and all of the elements in this family, have four valence electrons. In this case, each of these valence electrons are shared with a single half-filled orbital on each of the bromide atoms. Thus, the overall geometry is of an AB_4 grouping.

44. What is the bond angle(s) for tin tetrabromide? Is tin tetrabromide planar?

In problem 43 we established that tin tetrabromide is tetrahedral. Tetrahedral structures have about a 109^0 bond angle and they are not planar.

45. Which bond is the most polar? C-F; C-Cl; C-Br; C-I?

The most polar bond will have the greatest difference in electronegativity between the two atoms forming the bond. The EN for carbon is 2.5. The EN for F is 4; for Cl it is 3.0; for Br is it is 2.8 and for I it is 2.5. The greatest difference is found for C-F so it is the most polar bond.

46. For the bonds given in problem 45, which bond is the least polar?

From the information given in the answer to problem 45 the least difference is for C-I so it is the least polar bond.

47. Which of the following compounds is ionic? NO; CBr_4; $LINO_3$; SBr_4

The bond between Li and NO_3 is ionic though the bonding in the NO_3^- unit is covalent. The other bonds are covalent.

48. Since oxygen generally forms two bonds, what would you expect the bonding in an oxygen molecule to be?

O=O

49. There is a saying that atoms cannot have more than eight electrons about them. This is referred to as the octet rule. Many compounds have more than eight electrons about them. How is this possible?

In the quantum chemistry triangle we have

1s
2s   2p
3s   3p   3d
4s   4p   4d   4f

The octet rule applies to the second row elements because they have only s and p orbitals that are available for bonding. But elements in the third and higher rows also have d (and for higher rows other available orbitals) available to accommodate additional electrons. Thus, they "expand" the octet to beyond eight.

50. Which of the following compounds has more than eight electrons about the central atom? CCl_4; SBr_4; SI_6; CO_2; KI

SBr_4 and SI_6 have more than eight electrons about the sulfur atom.

51. How many electrons are about Xe in $XeBr_6$?

There are six sigma bonds, each with two electrons giving a total of 12 electrons about Xe. Plus an unbonded electron pair making 14.

52. Which of the following has the same electron pair geometry as sulfur tetrabromide?
SeI_4; SCl_4; $AsBr_4^-$; SnI_4^{-2}

All of them have the same electron pair geometry. They all have central atoms with six electrons forming four sigma bonds with the surrounding halides and a single unbonded electron pair.

53. What is the electron pair geometry for $XeBr_4$?

    Octahedral. Xe has eight valence electrons. Four of the valence electrons are bonded to the four bromides leaving four unbonded electrons that form two unbonded electron pairs. Thus, the overall geometry is AB_6.

54. What is the molecular geometry for xenon tetrabromide?

    The molecules given in problems 53 and 54 are the same. In 53 we established that the electron pair geometry was octahedral with two unbonded electron pairs. Thus, it has a molecular pair geometry of a square planar.

55. Remembering that carbon typically forms four bonds, either to two, three, or four different atoms, predict the structure for ethylene, C_2H_4. Hint, the carbon atoms are bonded to one another.

    The structure is $H_2C=CH_2$ with sigma bonds formed between the two carbon atoms and between each hydrogen atom and carbon; and a second bond formed between the two carbon atoms.

56. List the following in order of increasing electronegativity. C, B, O, F, Be

    Electronegativity increases as we move from the left of a row to the right and as we move from the bottom of a family to the top of a family. This is inverse to size. Thus, the correct order is Be<B<C<O<F.

57. Which of the following does not contain both an ionic and covalent bond? $Ca(OH)_2$; $LiNO_3$; $BaSO_4$; $SrCO_3$

    All of the contain both ionic bonds, between the polyatomic ions, and covalent bonding within the polyatomic ions.

58. What would you expect to be the formula from the reaction of an aluminum ion and selenium ion?

    Aluminum ions will generally be +3 and the Se ions will generally be a −2 so that the formula will be Al_2S_3.

59. Which of the following has the most unbonded electron pairs about the central atom?

    SBr_2; SI_6; SCl_4; SBr_2^{-2}

    SBr_2^{-2} has the most; it has 3 unbonded electron pairs.

60. For the compound HONO where nitrogen is the central atom, what is the electron pair geometry about nitrogen?

    Nitrogen has 5 valence electrons. Oxygen likes to form two bonds, either with the same atom, as here with one of the oxygen atoms N=O; or with two different atoms as in H-O-N. This leaves one unbonded electron pair on the nitrogen. Thus, the geometry about the nitrogen is trigonal planar.

SAMPLE TEST PROBLEMS

Name _____   Date _____

Circle only correct answers.

61. What is the molecular shape of aluminum tribromide?

    a. pyramidal; b. T-shaped; c. triangular planar; d. see-saw; e. linear.

62. What is the molecular geometry of sulfur hexachloride?

    a. see-saw; b. T-shaped; c. linear; d. octahedral; e. pyramidal.

63. What is the approximate bond angle(s) in water?

    a. 360 degrees; b. 109 degrees; c. 90 degrees; d. 120, 90, and 180 degrees; e. 180 degrees.

64. What electron pair geometry has bond angles of 120 degrees?

    a. triangular planar; b. tetrahedral; c. octahedral; d. T-shaped; e. see-saw.

65. What is the electron pair geometry for methane, CH_4, pictured below?

    a. see-saw; b. square planar; c. tetrahedral; d. bent; e. octahedral.

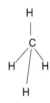

66. Water has _____ unbonded electron pairs about oxygen.

    a. 1; b. 2; c. 3; d. 4; e. 5.

67. Tin dichloride, $SnCl_2$, has only two atoms surrounding the central tin atom. Why then is the tin dichloride molecule bent?

    a. It is bent only periodically as it swings between both bent and linearshapes; b lone pairs of electrons on the chlorine atoms push it to this orientation; c. a lone pair of electrons on tin pushed it to this orientation; d. there is a covalent bond between the two chlorine atoms; e. tin dichloride is an ionic compound so takes on a bent geometry because there is one tin atom for every two chlorine atoms.

68. Which atom is the largest?

    a. B; b. Li; c. P; d. Cs; e. K?

69. Which of the following electron pair geometries are planar?

    a. tetrahedral; b. linear; c. octahedral; d. triangular pyramidal; e. triangular bipyramidal.

70. What is the molecular geometry for the ammonium ion?

    a. linear; b. triangular planar; c. octahedral; d. tetrahedral; e. T-shape.